TEACHER'S ANNOTATED EDITION

Vocabulary Workshop
New Edition

Level Blue

W9-CEL-721

Jerome Shostak

Consultants

Virginia M. Russell
Director of Clinical Experiences
Hunter College, School of Education
New York, NY

Elaine M. Czarnecki
Literacy Consultant
Annapolis, MD

Diane Flora
Reading Specialist
Indianapolis, IN

Sadlier-Oxford
A Division of William H. Sadlier, Inc.

Vocabulary Workshop
New Edition

Reviewers

The publisher wishes to thank the following teachers for their thorough review and thoughtful comments on portions of the series prior to publication.

Sharon West
Fifth Grade Teacher
Tallahassee, FL

Patty Bowman
Fifth Grade Teacher
Plano, TX

Debbie Dantin
Fifth Grade Teacher
Marrero, LA

Printed in the United States of America.
ISBN: 0-8215-0375-8
123456789/10 09 08 07 06

CONTENTS

Vocabulary Workshop Level Blue

Introduction to the New Edition

Today, more than ever, vocabulary instruction is recognized as critical to success in reading. Research confirms that word knowledge is essential to reading comprehension and that it is the best indicator of how well a reader will understand what he or she reads. The more words that a student masters, the more accomplished he or she will be as a reader and as a writer.

This **New Edition** of VOCABULARY WORKSHOP Level Blue both reflects current research in vocabulary instruction and provides fifth-grade teachers with an effective, easy-to-use tool for increasing their students' working vocabulary. The **New Edition** also introduces in the Review sections several features designed to make VOCABULARY WORKSHOP more effective than ever as preparation for vocabulary- and writing-related parts of standardized tests.

■ **Vocabulary for Comprehension** gives students practice in the kind of passage-based comprehension and vocabulary questions that appear on standardized tests.

■ A new **Grammar in Context** feature, which follows the Vocabulary for Comprehension exercise, refers to an example of grammar, usage, or mechanics illustrated in the reading passage and gives instruction and practice in that skill.

■ **Completing the Idea** invites students to use the new vocabulary they have learned to complete sentence stems. The open-ended **Write Your Own** feature that concludes the exercise encourages students to use a vocabulary word in a correctly written sentence.

■ **Building with Latin and Greek Roots** introduces students to families of English words that derive from common Latin or Greek stems.

This **New Edition** of VOCABULARY WORKSHOP Level Blue also includes new program components designed to supplement the Student Text and to furnish teachers with additional assessment options and other resources.

■ **Interactive Online Activities,** available on the Sadlier-Oxford Web site at **www.sadlier-oxford.com**, provide students with engaging word puzzles and games using the vocabulary presented in the Student Text.

■ **Online Teacher Resources,** such as graphic organizers, also available at **www.sadlier-oxford.com**, furnish teachers with materials that they can use to complement, extend, and enrich the instruction contained in the Student Text.

In the following pages of the Teacher's Edition, you will learn more about the VOCABULARY WORKSHOP program, including these new features and components, as well as how to get the most out of the **New Edition** of Level Blue for your students.

Instructional Approach

The direct-instruction approach of **VOCABULARY WORKSHOP** Level Blue is based on the latest research in the areas of vocabulary development and vocabulary skills. Level Blue provides instruction both in specific words and in word-learning strategies.

VOCABULARY WORKSHOP Level Blue focuses on 192 core words—their meanings, their ranges of application, and their relationships to other words. At the same time, the instructional approach recognizes the importance of textual context in the acquisition of vocabulary and in proper usage of words.

One of the cornerstones of the pedagogical approach taken in **VOCABULARY WORKSHOP** is intensive reinforcement through varied and abundant exercises. This method provides students with maximum exposure to different meanings of the words studied and maximum coverage of their applicability.

Word List

At the heart of Level Blue are the 192 core words. These words have been selected according to the following criteria:

- Frequency of appearance on recognized vocabulary lists
- Applicability to standardized tests
- Current grade-placement research
- General usefulness in both oral and written communication

The list of core words for Level Blue has been developed from many sources, including spelling and vocabulary lists; current subject-area textbooks, glossaries, and ancillary materials (especially for general, nontechnical terms); and classics and contemporary fiction and nonfiction.

Program Components

The Student Text contains 16 Units of 12 words each. The Units provide multiple exposures to, and practice with, the 192 core words. Four Reviews and 2 Cumulative Reviews provide enrichment and extension features, as well as preparation for vocabulary-related skills assessed on standardized tests. Formal assessment appears in the form of a Diagnostic Test and a Final Mastery Test.

The **Teacher's Edition** contains the answers to all exercise items in the Student Text and the (optional) Test Booklets. In addition, it offers useful information about the program and how to put it into practice in the classroom.

Two **Test Booklets** (optional purchase) for Level Blue provide supplemental practice and additional assessment options.

Interactive Online Activities, available on the Sadlier-Oxford Web site at **www.sadlier-oxford.com**, are designed to provide students with engaging interactive puzzles and games using the vocabulary presented in Level Blue.

Online Teacher Resources, also available on the Sadlier-Oxford Web site, furnish teachers with materials that can be used to complement, extend, and enrich the instruction contained in the Student Text.

Research-Based Program

Research has long shown that vocabulary plays a critical role in learning to read and comprehend text and, therefore, in children's success in school (Biemiller, 2003; Davis, 1942; Whipple, 1925). Not only does vocabulary improve reading comprehension, as research has confirmed (Nagy, 1988), but it also supports student's writing and speaking, as well as learning in the content areas. **VOCABULARY WORKSHOP** Level Blue is designed to promote vocabulary acquisition with an instructional approach that is supported by reading research. (A fuller discussion of current research in vocabulary instruction and practices can be found in the Sadlier-Oxford Professional Development Paper *Vocabulary Instruction in the Elementary Grades*. For more information, visit the Sadlier-Oxford Web site at **www.sadlier-oxford.com**.)

THE RESEARCH

How Do Students Learn New Vocabulary Words?

Researchers agree that although extensive reading is important to vocabulary growth, direct instruction is more effective and more efficient than incidental learning in achieving deeper, richer levels of lasting vocabulary understanding (McKeown & Beck, 1988). Stahl and Fairbanks (1986) recommend using a definitional and contextual approach to direct instruction, and Nagy (1988) recommends including integration, repetition, and meaningful use.

Vocabulary Workshop

VOCABULARY WORKSHOP Level Blue provides direct instruction for 192 carefully selected words. These words are introduced in Units that give concise definitions and examples of usage and then provide exercise sets that have students see and use the words in a variety of contexts. To promote repetition, students must use (by writing or choosing) each word five times over the course of a Unit; and in the Word Associations exercises that conclude the Units, students are asked to demonstrate meaningful use of the words by making inferences from the definitions and from the examples of usage.

THE RESEARCH

What Principles Should Guide Vocabulary Instruction?

If students are truly to gain ownership of new words, vocabulary instruction must provide multiple and varied encounters with those words (Daniels, 1994, 1996; Leung, 1992; Senechal, 1997; Stahl & Fairbanks, 1986). Current research (National Reading Panel, 2000) also suggests other practices that should inform the way vocabulary is taught in the classroom; these include using multiple methods of instruction and actively engaging students in word learning.

Vocabulary Workshop

First in the Units and then in the Reviews and Cumulative Reviews, **VOCABULARY WORKSHOP** Level Blue provides students with multiple exposures to all the taught words. These exposures, moreover, appear in a variety of contexts that represent as fully as possible each word's semantic range and application. **VOCABULARY WORKSHOP** also provides activities in which students are active participants. They are encouraged to act out words through games, and they complete sentence starters with their own ideas. Review activities, games, and puzzles complement formal instruction.

THE RESEARCH

What Word-Learning Strategies Are Beneficial to Students?

According to *Put Reading First* (Armbruster, Lehr, & Osborn, 2001), children need to develop effective word-learning strategies that include using information about word parts to figure out the meaning of words in text and using context clues to determine word meanings. According to Aranoff (1994), morphological knowledge (the strategy that focuses on the structure of a word) helps students to determine the meaning of an unfamiliar word that is derived from the same stem as a word they already know. Effective vocabulary teaching should therefore include direct instruction in roots, as well as prefixes and suffixes.

Vocabulary Workshop

VOCABULARY WORKSHOP Level Blue provides students with instruction in and practice with words derived from the same Latin or Greek roots as words to which they have been introduced in the Units. Students are also given explicit instruction and ample practice in the strategy of using context to determine the meaning of an unknown word, as well as opportunities to apply this strategy in the sentence-completion exercises that appear in every Unit and Cumulative Review.

References

Armbruster, B. B., Lehr, F., & Osborn, J. (2001). *Put reading first: The research building blocks for teaching children to read, kindergarten through grade 3.* Jessup, MD: Partnership for Reading.

Aranoff, M. (1994). Morphology. In A. C. Purves, L. Papa, & S. Jordan (Eds.), *Encyclopedia of English studies and language arts* (Vol. II, pp. 820–821). New York, NY: Scholastic.

Biemiller, A. (2003). *Vocabulary: Needed if more children are to read well.* Reading Psychology, 24(3–4), 323–335.

Daniels, M. (1996). Bilingual, bimodal education for hearing kindergarten students. *Sign Language Studies,* 90, 25–37.

Davis, F. B. (1942). Two new measures of reading ability. *Journal of Educational Psychology,* 33, 365–372.

Leung, C. B. (1992). Effects of word-related variables on vocabulary growth repeated read-aloud events. In C. K. Kinzer & D. J. Leu (Eds.), *Literacy research, theory, and practice: Views from many perspectives.* Forty-first Yearbook of the National Reading Conference (pp. 491–498). Chicago, IL: The National Reading Conference.

McKeown, M. G., & Beck, I. L. (1988). Learning vocabulary: Different ways for different goals. *Remedial and Special Education,* 9(1), 42–46.

Nagy, W. E. (1988). *Teaching vocabulary to improve reading comprehension.* Newark, DE: International Reading Association.

Nagy, W. E., & Scott, J. A. (2000). Vocabulary processes. In M. L. Kamil, P. G. Mosenthal, P. D. Pearson, & R. Barr (Eds.), *Handbook of reading research* (Vol. III, pp. 269–284). Mahwah, NJ: Lawrence Erlbaum Associates.

National Reading Panel. (2000). *Teaching children to read: An evidence-based assessment of the scientific research literature on reading and its implications for reading instruction.* Washington, DC: National Institute of Child Health and Human Development.

Senechal, M. (1997). The differential effect of storybook reading on preschoolers' acquisition of expressive and receptive vocabulary. *Journal of Child Language,* 24(1), 123–128.

Stahl, S. A., & Fairbanks, M. M. (1986). The effects of vocabulary instruction: A model-based meta-analysis. *Review of Educational Research,* 56(1), 72–110.

Whipple, G. (Ed.). (1925). *The twenty-fourth yearbook of the national society for the study of education: Report of the national committee on reading.* Bloomington, IL: Public School Publishing Company.

SUPPORTING ENGLISH LANGUAGE LEARNERS

In some of today's classrooms, students come from diverse backgrounds with varying degrees of English proficiency. Following are suggestions that will support English language learners in their acquisition of vocabulary.

To help English language learners develop vocabulary:

■ Use realia, pictures, gestures, and facial expressions to teach words and clarify meaning.

■ Teach words that are essential for understanding a story, but also focus on basic words—words that a native speaker in the elementary grades would not necessarily need to learn.

■ Provide scaffolding by having students choose from a list of words to complete partially finished sentences and paragraphs. Ask students who have a better command of English to define words, use words in sentences, and answer questions that involve those words.

■ Encourage active participation, repeating directions and modeling how to perform the tasks. Be patient. Remember that because of cultural differences, students may be reluctant to participate.

■ Model proper usage, and correct errors judiciously. Use corrections to positively reinforce students' use of English.

■ Focus on vocabulary instruction several times during the day, integrating vocabulary development with other lessons. Encourage students to use English as much as possible to gain confidence over time.

■ Encourage Spanish-speaking English language learners to use their knowledge of Spanish vocabulary to help read words in English that share the same cognates.

It is important to remember that cultural differences can affect how students learn and behave in the classroom. To provide the best possible learning environment for these students, teachers need to be culturally sensitive and aware of the implications of these differences.

ASSESSMENT OPTIONS

There are many ways to assess students' knowledge of the words in **VOCABU-LARY WORKSHOP** Level Blue. The informal and formal assessment suggestions below can provide insight into students' understanding of the words.

Informal Assessment

■ **Oral Language** Observe whether students use the taught words in conversations and in classroom discussions.

■ **Student Writing** Observe whether students attempt to use the taught words in their writing.

■ **Daily Use** Observe whether students recognize the taught words when they see them in print or hear them on television or radio.

■ **Vocabulary Notebook** Observe how students expand their knowledge of the taught words.

For an extended discussion on how to implement these suggestions, see pages T13–T17, T19–T26, and T28–T33.

Formal Assessment

Student Text

■ **Diagnostic Test** The Diagnostic Test on pages 10–11 of the Student Text can be used to assess students' vocabulary knowledge at the beginning of the school year. It can also serve as a before-and-after comparison when combined with the Final Mastery Test.

■ **Cumulative Review** The Cumulative Reviews on pages 76–83 and 148–155 of the Student Text can be used to assess students' knowledge of the words in Units 1–8 and 9–16, respectively. Students' responses can give insight into their word knowledge to date. The exercises can also serve as reinforcement.

■ **Final Mastery Test** The Final Mastery Test on pages 156–159 of the Student Text can be used to assess students' knowledge of the words in Units 1–16. This test will show how much progress has been made during the school year. It too can serve as a reinforcement exercise.

Test Booklets (Optional Purchase)

The two Supplementary Test Booklets follow the organization of the Student Text. A Unit Test is provided for each of the 16 Units, a Mastery Test corresponds to each of the 4 Reviews, and a Final Mastery Test supplements the test in the Student Text.

Developing Vocabulary Through Literature

VOCABULARY WORKSHOP Level Blue can be combined with the titles listed below to form a literature-based approach to vocabulary study. Seeing the words they are studying in classic and contemporary literature can reinforce students' appreciation of the value of possessing a strong vocabulary.

Literature to Use with the Program

Author	Title	Type
Babbit, Natalie	*The Search for Delicious*	Fantasy/Dictionary Definitions
Banks, Lynne Reid	*The Indian in the Cupboard*	Fantasy/Adventure
Brink, Carol Ryrie	*Caddie Woodlawn*	Historical/Prairie
Brittain, Bill	*The Wish Giver*	Mystery/Suspense
Burnford, Shirley	*The Incredible Journey*	Animal/Adventure
Byars, Betsy	*Summer of the Swans*	Realistic/Family
Clement, Andrew	*Frindle*	Realistic/History of Language
Conrad, Pam	*Our House*	Short Stories/Humor/Levittown
Curtis, Christopher Paul	*The Watsons Go to Birmingham–1963*	Historical/African American
Dorris, Michael	*Morning Girl*	Historical/Native American
Fitzgerald, John D.	*The Great Brain*	Realistic/Humor
Fitzhugh, Louise	*Harriet the Spy*	Realistic/Humor
George, Jean Craighead	*My Side of the Mountain*	Adventure/Survival
Gipson, Frederick	*Old Yeller*	Animal/Realistic
Gray, Lulu	*Falcon's Egg*	Fantasy/Family
King-Smith, Dick	*School Mouse*	Animal/Books & Reading
Konigsburg, E.L.	*The View From Saturday*	Realistic/Language Contest
Lofting, Hugh	*The Story of Doctor Doolittle*	Animal/Fantasy/Adventure
Lord, Betty Bao	*In the Year of the Boar and Jackie Robinson*	Historical/Chinese American
Lowry, Lois	*Number the Stars*	Historical/WWII
MacLachlan, Patricia	*Sarah, Plain and Tall* *The Facts and Fictions of Minna Pratt*	Historical/Prairie Realistic/Musicians
Merrill, Jean	*The Pushcart War*	Realistic/Humor
Mohr, Nicholasa	*Felita*	Realistic/Hispanic
Naylor, Phyllis Reynolds	*Shiloh*	Realistic/Animal
North, Sterling	*Rascal*	Autobiography/Animal/Humor
Norton, Mary	*The Borrowers*	Fantasy/Family
Snyder, Zilpha Keatley	*Cat Running*	Historical/Great Depression/ Dust Bowl
Steig, William	*Dominic*	Animal/Humor/Fantasy
Tate, Eleanor	*Thank You, Dr. Martin Luther King Jr.*	Historical/Realistic
Taylor, Sidney	*All-of-a-Kind Family*	Historical Fiction/NYC/Jewish
Woodson, Jacqueline	*Last Summer with Maizon*	African American/Friendship/ Realistic

Pacing Chart

The **VOCABULARY WORKSHOP** program is designed to be used with any Reading and Language Arts program. Its format is simple and allows for great flexibility. Activity assignments can be adjusted to conform to the special needs of any class. The chart below shows how various components of the program might be scheduled over an academic year.

Week	Student Text	Follow-Up Activities
1–2	Vocabulary of Vocabulary, pp. 5–8 Pronunciation Key, p. 9 Diagnostic Test, pp. 10–11	
3 4 5 6	Unit 1, pp. 12–17 Unit 2, pp. 18–23 Unit 3, pp. 24–29 Unit 4, pp. 30–35	Activities on pp. T13–T17 Online games and activities Units 1–4 Tests*
7	Review (Units 1–4), pp. 36–43	Activities on pp. T19–T26 Online games and activities Mastery Test Units 1–4*
8 9 10 11	Unit 5, pp. 44–49 Unit 6, pp. 50–55 Unit 7, pp. 56–61 Unit 8, pp. 62–67	Activities on pp. T13–T17 Online games and activities Units 5–8 Tests*
12	Review (Units 5–8), pp. 68–75	Activities on pp. T19–T26 Online games and activities Mastery Test Units 5–8*
13	Cumulative Review I (Units 1–8), pp. 76–83	Activities on pp. T28–T33
14 15 16 17	Unit 9, pp. 84–89 Unit 10, pp. 90–95 Unit 11, pp. 96–101 Unit 12, pp. 102–107	Activities on pp. T13–T17 Online games and activities Units 9–12 Tests*
18	Review (Units 9–12), pp. 108–115	Activities on pp. T19–T26 Online games and activities Mastery Test Units 9–12*
19 20 21 22	Unit 13, pp. 116–121 Unit 14, pp. 122–127 Unit 15, pp. 128–133 Unit 16, pp. 134–139	Activities on pp. T13–T17 Online games and activities Units 13–16 Tests*
23	Review (Units 13–16), pp. 140–147	Activities on pp. T19–T26 Online games and activities Mastery Test Units 13–16*
24	Cumulative Review II (Units 9–16), pp. 148–155	Activities on pp. T28–T33
25	Final Mastery Test (Units 1–16), pp. 156–159	Final Mastery Test Units 1–16*

*Available in the Supplementary Test Booklets

THE UNIT

Each Unit is divided into a unique 5-part structure designed to give maximum coverage to each of the key words within the space available.

Overview

Definitions	In Definitions, students are introduced to the 12 words in the Unit. After learning about the various elements associated with a word, students complete the sample sentence(s) showing how the word is used. The definitions provided are deliberately brief. The intent is to give students a reasonably good core idea of what each word means.
Match the Meaning	In Match the Meaning, students are given 4 taught words (all the same part of speech) and choose the word indicated by the clue. This set of exercises is designed to reinforce the students' understanding and recall of the words' meanings.
Synonyms and Antonyms	In Synonyms, students select the taught word that is the synonym for the highlighted word in an illustrative phrase. In Antonyms, students choose the antonym for the highlighted word. If the selected word is an antonym, the highlighted word is one listed as such in the Definitions section; if it is a synonym, the word is either part of a definition or listed as a synonym in the Definitions section.
Completing the Sentence	In Completing the Sentence, students use context clues to choose the word that logically and meaningfully completes each sentence. The sentences are loosely connected by a theme in various content areas, including Social Studies, Science, and the Arts.
Word Associations	In Word Associations, students demonstrate their understanding of the words by applying what they have learned about the words in a way that calls for a measure of inference, reasoning, perception, and imagination. Students complete a set of challenging exercises comprised of sentence completions and questions, each containing a highlighted taught word. They choose the answer that best completes the sentence or answers the question.

Because each unit has the same 5-part structure, the teaching notes on pages T13–T17 can be used for all such parts in a given unit.

DEFINITIONS

Teach

■ Discuss the structure and content of the Definitions pages. Explain that there are 12 words and that associated with each word are these elements: the pronunciation of the word, its part of speech, its definition, a sample sentence showing how the word is used, and a list of synonyms and antonyms for the word. Point out that some words can be used as different parts of speech and can have more than one meaning. For example, *document* (Unit 1) has one meaning when used as a verb and another meaning when used as a noun. (See page T29 for a more thorough discussion of multiple-meaning words.)

■ To help students develop a deeper understanding of the unit words, generate a discussion that gets at the character of the word and how it is typically used. For example, for *fragile* (Unit 1), ask:

- "Is a china teacup *fragile*? Explain."
- "Is an egg *fragile*? Explain."
- "Can you think of a kind of egg that isn't *fragile*?"
- "Name some other things that are *fragile*."
- "If you send something *fragile* in the mail, how would you pack it?"
- "Show me how you would carry something *fragile*."

■ Summarize by explaining the meaning of *fragile* using everyday language.

> MODEL From our discussion we know that something *fragile* can be easily damaged or broken and that it may require special care or handling. If you drop a crystal bowl, it will probably break because it is *fragile*.

Practice/Apply

■ Assign the two Definitions pages. Remind students to think about the explanations of the words as they complete the sentences. Then have them read the completed sentence silently.

Follow-Up

■ **Oral Language** To encourage daily use of the unit words, list them on a Word Wall. Encourage students to use the words in their speaking and writing. When they read, tell them to be alert to the words they have learned and to notice how the words are used.

■ **ELL** Model how to pronounce each unit word. Have students practice saying the words to an adult or another student. They should also say a sentence using each word. Guide students as needed.

 Additional vocabulary games and activities can be found online at **www.sadlier-oxford.com** .

MATCH THE MEANING

Teach

■ To help students process the meanings of the unit words, have them interact with the words and relate them to their own experiences. For example, for the word *cancel* (Unit 1), have students describe a time when they had to *cancel* something they had planned to do. Give an example to get students started.

> **Model** Last week my family planned to go on a picnic. But when the day came, it rained so hard that we had to *cancel* our outing.

■ Lead other discussions that get students thinking about the words and how they are related. For example:

- For the word *veteran* (Unit 1), ask, "To inspect the trails after a snow storm, do you think the ski patrol should rely on a *veteran* or a newcomer? Why?"
- For the word *strategy* (Unit 2), ask, "Do you need a *strategy* to write a research paper? To watch a movie? Explain."
- For the word *blunder* (Unit 1), say, "Describe a *blunder* you have made. What did you do when you realized your mistake?"
- For the word *impressive* (Unit 2), say, "Tell me about a person whose achievements are *impressive*."
- For the word *dispute* (Unit 2), ask, "What might you and a friend have a *dispute* about?"

Practice/Apply

■ Assign the Match the Meaning page. Tell students to think about the meaning of each choice before choosing the answer. When they finish, have students read the completed sentences to be sure they make sense.

Follow-Up

■ **Word Play** Have students make an acrostic poem using one of the unit words. Ask them to brainstorm a list of words or phrases that describe or remind them of the word. Then have them use the words to write the acrostic poem. The poem should be about the word, and each line should begin with a letter from the word. For example:

m ay be an ancient tale

y ou have heard it many times

t eaches or explains something

h ard to forget

SYNONYMS AND ANTONYMS

Teach

■ Tell students that learning synonyms and antonyms can help them expand their vocabulary. Explain that synonyms are words that have the same or similar meanings; for example, *fistfight* and *scuffle* (Unit 1) are synonyms.

> **Model** Instead of saying, "The coach broke up the *fistfight* between the two players," I can say, "The coach broke up the *scuffle* between the two players." The words *fistfight* and *scuffle* are synonyms. They both mean about the same thing.

■ Provide other sentences with *scuffle*. Ask students to give synonyms that could replace the word. Remind students that the synonym must make sense in the sentence.

■ Explain that antonyms are words with opposite meanings; for example, *distribute* (Unit 1) and *gather* are antonyms. Elicit from students other words that are the opposite of *distribute*. Guide them by providing sentences such as "Today I will *distribute* the test booklets." Ask students to replace *distribute* with a word that is opposite in meaning and that would make sense in the sentence. (*collect*)

■ Use other examples of synonyms and antonyms that are related to students' experiences.

■ To help students expand their vocabulary, revisit and discuss the synonyms and antonyms on the Definitions pages. Have students use some of the words in sentences. Encourage them to relate the words to their own experiences.

Practice/Apply

■ Assign the Synonyms/Antonyms page. Tell students to read each phrase and consider each choice before choosing their answer. Remind them to substitute their choice for the word in boldface to be sure it makes sense.

Follow-Up

■ **Expanding Vocabulary** Have students begin a Vocabulary Notebook in which they write down the meanings of the taught words and add to them as they learn more about the words. For example, have them list additional synonyms and antonyms.

■ **Writing** Have students list the unit words in their Vocabulary Notebook by part of speech. If they wish, students might also list synonyms and antonyms for the unit words. Students can choose from these synonyms and antonyms to make their writing more interesting.

COMPLETING THE SENTENCE

Teach

■ Engage students further in their work with word meanings. Provide cloze sentences with enough context for them to figure out which unit word correctly completes a sentence.

■ Tell students that context clues are clues that help us determine the meaning of an unfamiliar word. Explain that context clues can come in sentences before or after the unfamiliar word and that sometimes the context clue is a single word located within the same sentence.

■ Write the following on the board:

An all-sports channel on cable TV usually provides _____ coverage of events such as the Olympic Games.

> **MODEL** To figure out the unit word that fits in the sentence, I look for clues in the sentence. The words *all-sports channel* and *the Olympic Games* make me think that *continuous* (Unit 1) is the correct word. I know that an all-sports channel broadcasts nothing except sports. I also know that the Olympic Games take place over many days. When I read the sentence with the word *continuous*, it makes sense.

Practice/Apply

■ Briefly discuss the topics of the grouped sentences on the Completing the Sentence page. Then have students complete the page. Point out that as required by the sentence, the missing word may be the plural form of a noun or any tense or form (participial, for example) of a verb.

■ Have students tell what context clues they used to complete the sentences.

Follow-Up

■ **Informal Assessment** Distribute 12 copies of the Word Square below (available online at **www.sadlier-oxford.com**) to each student. Have students complete a Word Square page for each unit word.

WORD SQUARE

Word	My Connection
What It Means	**How It Looks**

WORD ASSOCIATIONS

Teach

■ Help students continue to build on the meanings of the unit words. Ask questions that require them to associate unit words with known words. For example, ask the following using the Unit 1 words *solitary*, *fragile*, and *continuous*.

- "Which word would you use to describe a person who lives alone, *fragile* or *solitary*? Explain."
- "Would you expect a highway to be *continuous* or *fragile*? Explain."

■ In another activity, show how you might connect a unit word to another word or phrase. For example:

myth	birth certificate
blunder	unicorn
document	clumsy move

> **MODEL** I know that a *myth* is something that is imaginary. A *unicorn* is a creature like a horse, but it has a long horn sticking out from its forehead. I know that no such animal exists. So *myth* goes with *unicorn*.

■ Ask students to relate *blunder* and *document* to the remaining phrases and then explain the relationship.

Practice/Apply

■ Assign the Word Associations page. When students finish, have them explain the reasons for their choices. Ask them to tell what word(s) they associated with the words in boldface.

Follow-Up

■ **Expanding Vocabulary** Distribute copies of the Word Web (available online at **www.sadlier-oxford.com**) to students. Have them write the unit word or a phrase with the word in the center circle and then write other words or phrases they associate with it. They can add as many circles as they need.

WORD WEB

TV series — magazine subscription — cancel — doctor's appointment — delivery

THE REVIEW

Each sequence of 4 Units is followed by a Review that covers only the words taught in those Units. The Reviews are designed to provide additional exposure to the taught words and to allow students to apply and expand their word knowledge.

Overview

Selecting Word Meanings	In Selecting Word Meanings, students match a taught word with a synonym or synonymous phrase.
Spelling and Antonyms	In Spelling, students decide if a taught word is correctly spelled. In Antonyms, students identify an antonym for a taught word.
Vocabulary for Comprehension	In Vocabulary for Comprehension, students read a passage that incorporates 5 of the taught words. After reading, students answer questions based on the passage.
Grammar in Context	In Grammar in Context, students practice selected grammar, usage, and mechanics skills that help them improve their writing.
Completing the Idea	In Completing the Idea, students apply their knowledge of word meanings by completing a writing activity. They relate their prior knowledge or a personal experience to a sentence starter that contains a taught word and then complete the thought.
Word Families	In Word Families, students expand and enrich their vocabularies. The word families are built on taught words, and students learn that these words are related in meaning.
Word Games	In Word Games, students complete games and puzzles.

With the exception of Grammar in Context, all 4 Reviews follow the same organization and feature the same types of exercises. As such, the teaching notes for these exercises can be used for all such exercises in the Review. On pages T22–T23, Grammar in Context, specific teaching notes are provided for the different grammar skills.

SELECTING WORD MEANINGS   SPELLING

SELECTING WORD MEANINGS

Teach

■ Review the taught words of the preceding 4 Units by having students give their meanings. Then present a phrase containing a taught word—for example, "*cancel my subscription to the newspaper*." Model how to determine which of the following words, *scuffle, reject, discontinue,* or *associate*, has nearly the same meaning as *cancel*.

Practice/Apply

■ Assign the Selecting Word Meanings page.

Follow-Up

■ **Word Play** Provide a set of word cards and a set of cards with the definitions of the words. Have pairs of students play a game of Concentration to reinforce the meanings of the words.

SPELLING

Teach

■ Say the taught words. Emphasize the phonetic sounds, pointing out the spelling(s) that stand for each sound. Tell students that using sound-spelling relationships can help them spell words.

■ Write a phrase such as the following on the board: "overcome the ob_tacle." Point out that the word with the blank is a taught word. Ask if the word is spelled correctly.

> **MODEL** The word looks like *obstacle*. But it is hard to say the word as spelled because the sound /s/ is missing. This tells me that the letter *s* might be missing. I try saying the word with /s/, and I find that now I am able to pronounce the word. The missing letter is *s*.

Practice/Apply

■ Assign the Spelling section of the page.

Follow-Up

■ **ELL** Provide word cards (available online at **www.sadlier-oxford.com**) for the taught words. Have students sort the words into groups you suggest, such as parts of speech or phonic elements. Or let students sort the words into groups of their own choosing. Have them share the sorts and the reasons for the word placements.

ANTONYMS

■ See the Antonyms section on page T15.

 Additional vocabulary games and activities can be found online at **www.sadlier-oxford.com**.

VOCABULARY FOR COMPREHENSION

■ Tell students that to understand what they are reading, they must know the meanings of the key words in the passage or be able to figure the meanings out. They must also use a variety of comprehension skills to help them grasp the meaning of the passage.

■ Present the paragraph and questions below.

On April 14, 1912, the *Titanic*, a magnificent ocean liner, hit an iceberg about 400 miles off Newfoundland, Canada. Nobody knew at first how bad the damage was. People were very calm. But soon it was clear that the ship was doomed. In less than three hours, the *Titanic* split into two pieces and sank into the deep, cold sea.

1. What is the main idea of the paragraph?
2. What details tell about the main idea?
3. What is the meaning of *doomed*?
4. What do you think happened to the people on board the ship?

■ Discuss the reading skills below. Model how to use them to answer the questions about the *Titanic*.

Identify Main Idea/Details The main idea of a passage is what the passage is about. It is the most important point that the author makes about a topic or subject. The main idea is often stated at the beginning of the passage. The rest of the passage usually gives details that help explain or support the main idea.

> **MODEL** To answer the first two questions about the *Titanic*, I use the information in the paragraph. The main idea tells me what the paragraph is about. From reading the paragraph, I know that it is mainly about the sinking of the *Titanic*. The details tell me when the *Titanic* sank (April 14, 1912), where it sank (about 400 miles off Newfoundland, Canada), and why it sank (hit an iceberg).

Vocabulary in Context Sometimes using context clues can help a reader figure out the meaning of a word. The clues can be in the surrounding sentences, or they can be other words in the sentence.

> **MODEL** To figure out the meaning of *doomed*, I look at the other words in the sentence and at the sentences that come before it. In the sentence with *doomed*, the word *but* tells me that the situation was not hopeful. This, together with the other clues, makes me think that *doomed* means "certain to fail or be destroyed."

Make Inferences Authors do not always state directly everything that happens in a passage. Instead, they provide details that allow readers to figure out things for themselves. Making inferences is using clues or details in the passage and the readers' prior knowledge to make logical decisions about events and actions that are not stated.

> **MODEL** To answer the last question, I put together everything that I know happened. I know that the *Titanic* hit an iceberg, and I know that the ship was doomed. The last sentence tells me that the *Titanic* split in two and sank. All this makes me think that the people on board drowned.

■ Using the paragraph, model how to monitor comprehension. Show how you would stop and reread to understand important details or what you might do to clarify confusing parts.

> **MODEL** The *Titanic* hit an iceberg about 400 miles off the coast of Newfoundland. It's hard to imagine what a distance of 400 miles is like. To help me better understand the situation, I will ask the librarian to help me find a map of the North Atlantic that shows the coast of Newfoundland. Then I will ask for help in pinpointing a distance that is about 400 miles off the coast.

Practice/Apply

■ Assign the Vocabulary for Comprehension pages. Tell students that on these pages, they are going to put their word knowledge and reading skills to use by reading a passage and then answering questions based on the passage. Point out that the passage and questions are similar to those they are likely to find on standardized tests. Tell them to read carefully and to be sure to base their answer choices on what they read. Point out that there may be answer choices that make sense but that are not based on the passage.

Follow-Up

■ **Writing** Have students add to the passage. The sentences or paragraph(s) may expand on the passage, or they may tell how students feel about what they read. Encourage students to use some of the taught words in their writing.

■ **Oral Language** Create a Word Wall of interesting words. Have students contribute new words encountered in their reading, in conversations, on TV, and in their daily experiences. Before adding a word, encourage students to tell where they found it and describe the situation in which it was used.

GRAMMAR IN CONTEXT

Teach

■ Tell students that grammar is a set of rules for speaking and writing and that using the rules of grammar will help them to clearly express their ideas and make their thoughts easier to understand.

Run-on Sentences   (Review Units 1–4, p. 40)

■ Explain that a run-on sentence is two or more sentences that run together. Call attention to the run-on sentence above the box on page 40 and discuss the two ways to correct it. Then have students read the run-on and the corrected sentence(s). Discuss which sentence(s) are easier to read and understand.

> **MODEL** In the run-on sentence, all the words run together. I can't tell where one idea ends and the next one begins. The two separate sentences and the compound sentence are easier to read. Each separate sentence has a clear start and end point, and the comma in the compound sentence tells me where to pause in my reading.

Compound Subjects and Predicates   (Review Units 5–8, p. 72)

■ Discuss that sometimes too many short sentences can make our writing sound choppy. Explain that one way to fix this is to combine sentences that have either the same predicate or the same subject.

> **MODEL** Look at the first two sentences in the first box on page 72. The subject in the first sentence is *teachers,* and the subject in the second sentence is *classmates.* The predicate in each sentence is the same. We can combine the sentences by joining the subjects with the word *and.* The subject in the new sentence, *teachers and classmates,* is a compound subject.

■ Explain that a compound predicate has two or more predicates with the same subject. Using the sentences in the second box, discuss how to combine sentences that result in a compound predicate.

Comparing with Adjectives   (Review Units 9–12, p. 112)

■ Review that an adjective describes a noun and that when we use an adjective to compare, we must use the correct form of the adjective. Discuss the sentences in the box on page 112.

> **MODEL** In the sentence "Ice Cave is larger than Lava Cave," we are comparing two things, so we use the *er* form of *large.* In the sentence "Carlsbad Caverns is the largest cave in New Mexico," we are comparing Carlsbad Caverns with all the caves in New Mexico, so we use the *est* form of *large.*

Subject-Verb Agreement (Review Units 13–16, p. 144)

■ Explain that a verb and its subject must agree in number. If the subject is singular, the verb must be singular. If the subject is plural, the verb must be plural. Point out the forms of the verb *be* in the table on page 144. Then discuss the subject-verb agreement in the sentences in the box.

> **MODEL** In the first sentence, the singular subject, *the crowd*, agrees with the singular verb *was*. In the second sentence, the subject is the plural pronoun *we*, which agrees with the plural verb *are*.

■ Have students explain the subject-agreement in the remaining sentences.

Practice/Apply

■ Assign the Grammar in Context page. Make sure students understand what to do before asking them to complete the page. When they finish, ask them to review their work. To make them more aware of words and how they are used, have students pay particular attention to the taught words in the exercises.

Follow-Up

Run-on Sentences (Review Units 1–4, p. 40)
■ **Writing** Post examples of run-on sentences from students' written work. Have students identify and correct the run-on sentences.

Compound Subjects and Predicates (Review Units 5–8, p. 72)
■ **Writing** Have students write two sentences with the same subject but different predicates or with the same predicate but different subjects. Have them exchange papers with partners, who will combine the sentences by joining the subjects or predicates that are the same.

Comparing with Adjectives (Review Units 9–12, p. 112)
■ **ELL** Have students compare two or three people or things. For example, have a student tell who is taller, person A or person B. Or have a student tell which of three things is the heaviest, item A, B, or C.

Subject-Verb Agreement (Review Units 13–16, p. 144)
■ **Oral Language** Begin a class story with a sentence such as: "Yesterday was the best day at school." Have each student add a sentence to move the story along. Tell students to be on the alert for correct subject-verb agreement as they say their sentences.

COMPLETING THE IDEA

Teach

■ To help make the taught words a permanent part of students' vocabulary, give them many opportunities to use and think about the words. Have students discuss and answer questions such as the following:

- "Can a *villain* be both *treacherous* and *cautious*? Explain."
- "When might it be necessary to *bluff* someone? Explain."
- "If a *mishap* occurs, would you apologize or blame someone else? Why?"

Tell students that any answer they can adequately support is acceptable. Model how you might answer the first question.

> MODEL A *villain* is someone who is wicked or evil. Such a person would probably betray another and so could be described as *treacherous*. A *villain* might also be likely to avoid taking unnecessary risks in carrying out his or her plans and so might be described as *cautious*.

Encourage students to offer other answers.

Practice/Apply

■ Assign the Completing the Idea page. Point out that the taught words in the sentence stem are in boldface. Tell students to think about the definition of each taught word and how to complete the idea meaningfully before they begin to write. Remind them that there is more than one correct way to complete an idea.

■ In Write Your Own, have students write a sentence using one of the taught words. The sentence should reflect the grammar skill they just learned.

Follow-Up

■ **Expanding Vocabulary** To instill an interest in words, have students keep track of unfamiliar words that they encounter in their independent reading. Have them select a few words and complete the My Words graphic organizer (available online at **www.sadlier-oxford.com**) for each word in order to learn as much as they can about it.

■ **ELL** To provide students with the opportunity to hear vocabulary words in context, dictate sentences that include the taught words. Ask students to touch each word in the sentence with their pencils as you repeat it. You might also tell students how many words are in the sentence and allow them time to count. Be sure to provide at least three opportunities for students to hear a sentence before moving on to the next one.

WORD FAMILIES

Teach

■ Use word families to build on students' knowledge of taught words. For example, write *luxurious*, *luxuriously*, and *luxuriousness* on the board. Point out the word *luxurious* in *luxuriously* and *luxuriousness*, and explain that all the words are related in meaning. If they know the meaning of *luxurious*, they can figure out the meaning of the other two words.

■ Explain that adding a word ending can affect the way a word is used in a sentence. It can change the part of speech of the word. For example, the adjective *luxurious* is changed to the adverb *luxuriously* when *ly* is added; it is changed to the noun *luxuriousness* when *ness* is added.

■ Show students how word families can help them figure out the meanings of new words. Write the following on the board: "Only a very rich person would be able to live so *luxuriously*."

> **MODEL** To figure out the meaning of *luxuriously*, I look for the word *luxurious* and recall that it means "providing ease and comfort far beyond what is ordinary or necessary." I use what I know about the meaning of *luxurious* to help me understand that "live so luxuriously" means "living in a way that is comfortable and pleasurable over and above what is really needed."

Practice/Apply

■ Assign the Word Families page. Using *emigrate/emigration* as an example, point out that sometimes the final *e* in a word is dropped when a word ending that begins with a vowel is added. Discuss the other common word endings found among the words in boldface in the exercises.

Follow-Up

■ **Expanding Vocabulary** Have students find related words for the words in the word box on the Word Families page. Some examples are given below.

Noun	Adjective	Verb	Adverb
flexibility	flexible		flexibly
caution	cautious		cautiously
postponement		to postpone (postpones, postponed, postponing)	

WORD GAMES

Teach

- To help students develop vocabulary, create an atmosphere in which they can have fun with words. For example, have students make up riddles such as the following:

  - Why did the star shine so brightly? Because it was _____. (brilliant)
  - What do you call a crafty fellow? (a shrewd dude)

Point out that the second riddle above is a hink pink. Explain that in a hink pink, the answer is a pair of rhyming words that matches a defining phrase in the riddle. The rhyming words are usually an adjective paired with a noun. Explain how to create a hink pink such as the one above.

> **MODEL** To create a hink pink, I start with an answer that is a pair of rhyming words—for example, *shrewd dude*. Then I think of synonyms for each word—for example, *crafty* for *shrewd* and *fellow* for *dude*. Then I write a question using the synonyms. But I have to remember that the question has to be worded in such a way that the answer *shrewd dude* makes sense.

- Have students work with partners to make up hink pinks and other riddles. Tell them that a taught word should be included in each answer.

Practice/Apply

- Assign the Word Games page. To help students narrow down the word choices, remind them that the words should be chosen from the 4 Units they just studied. In the puzzles on pages 43 and 147, point out that students have to unscramble the letters in the circles to find the answer to the Challenge question.

Follow-Up

- **Word Play** Have students create puzzles similar to the ones on the Word Games page. Encourage them to write clues that are concise but full explanations. Students can exchange and complete one another's puzzles.

- **Informal Assessment** Have students form two teams for a Vocabulary Bee. Give a definition for a taught word to a student on Team A. If the student correctly identifies the word, Team A scores a point. Continue with Team B. The first team to score 25 points wins. You might want to display the taught words on a chart or Word Wall for students to refer to.

THE CUMULATIVE REVIEW

Two Cumulative Reviews are provided in the Student Text. Cumulative Review I covers the words presented in the first half of the book (Units 1–8), and Cumulative Review II covers the words presented in the second half (Units 9–16). Like the Reviews, the Cumulative Reviews provide additional exposure to the unit words and give students the opportunity to expand their word knowledge.

Overview

Definitions and Antonyms	In Definitions and in Antonyms, students match definitions and antonyms to taught words.
Completing the Sentence	In Completing the Sentence, students choose from a limited number of words. The sentences are not thematically related.
Classifying	In Classifying, students look for a relationship among a group of words and choose the word that may be considered a member of the group.
Analogies	In Analogies, students find the relationship between a pair of words and explain it in a sentence. Most of the analogies are of a purely vocabulary-based nature; that is, the relationship between the key words is that of synonyms or antonyms.
Building with Latin and Greek Roots	In Building with Latin and Greek Roots, students determine a word's meaning by examining its root.

With the exception of Building with Latin and Greek Roots, both Cumulative Reviews follow the same organization and feature the same types of exercises. As such, the teaching notes for these exercises can be used for all such exercises in the Cumulative Review. On pages T32–T33, Building with Latin and Greek Roots, specific teaching notes are provided for the different roots.

DEFINITIONS
(CUMULATIVE REVIEW)

Teach

■ Review the words that students find challenging. For each word, ask a volunteer to tell everything he or she knows about it, including its meaning(s), synonyms, antonyms, and part(s) of speech. Then point out that the same elements can be found next to an entry in a dictionary.

■ Review that students can find the meanings of unfamiliar words in a dictionary. Present a dictionary, and review the way in which it is organized. Explain how to use guide words to help locate a word. Point out that in addition to the elements mentioned above, a word's pronunciation is also given.

Practice/Apply

■ Assign the Definitions page. Tell students to try identifying the word after they read the definition before attempting to find it in the word box. Have them cross out the words as they are used.

Follow-Up

■ **Writing** Have students create a dictionary of the taught words. Ask them to provide the guide words for each dictionary page.

ANTONYMS
(CUMULATIVE REVIEW)

Teach

■ To review antonyms for the taught words, have students play "Guess My Word." Provide word cards (available online at **www.sadlier-oxford.com**) for taught words that have antonyms. Have students pick a word and then give antonym clues for the word. For example, for the word *aggressive*, a clue might be "My word is an antonym for *timid*." To simplify the task, give 4 words from which students can choose.

Practice/Apply

■ Assign the Antonyms page. Point out that all the words in an exercise are similar in meaning. Students are to find the word in the box that is most nearly opposite in meaning to the group of words in each exercise.

Follow-Up

■ **Word Play** Provide each student with a Bingo game board. Ask students to write a taught word in each space. (You may want to have students choose their words from a prepared list of words that have antonyms.) Call out antonyms to some taught words. If the taught word is on a student's board, he or she puts a marker on it. A student shouts "Bingo!" when he or she has successfully filled a row, column, or diagonal.

COMPLETING THE SENTENCE
(CUMULATIVE REVIEW)

Teach

■ Remind students that some words have more than one meaning. Explain that when a multiple-meaning word is used in a sentence, they can figure out the intended meaning by using the context clues. Point out, however, that first they need to be familiar with the various meanings.

■ Write the following on the board for the word *associate* (Unit 4):
  • Many people prefer to *associate* with others who share similar interests.
  • Even today, I *associate* the smell of the ocean with summers at the beach when I was a child.

> **MODEL** If I didn't know the meaning of *associate*, I could look it up in a dictionary. When I look up *associate*, I see that there is more than one definition for the word. I read each definition and think about whether it fits the context of the sentence. After I decide on the correct meaning, I substitute the likely definition in the original sentence to see if it makes sense. In the first example, the clue "others who share" tells me that *associate* means "to be together as partners, allies, or friends." In the second example, the phrases "Even today" and "when I was a child" suggest something that connects past and present in the mind. So in this case, *associate* means "to link or connect in one's mind."

■ Review other taught words that have multiple meanings. Have students use the words in sentences to show their different meanings.

Practice/Apply

■ Assign the Completing the Sentence page. Tell students to use context clues to complete the sentences. Have them identify any multiple-meaning words on the page.

Follow-Up

■ **ELL** Provide practice with multiple-meaning words. For example, have students look for clues in the sentences below to help them figure out which meaning of *jolt* (Unit 6) is illustrated.

1. The train came to a screeching halt, *jolting* the passengers. ___ (b)
2. It gave me a *jolt* when my long-lost friend walked into the room. ___ (a)

a. a shock or surprise
b. to shake up roughly

You may want to have students act out the sentences to reinforce the various meanings of the words.

CLASSIFYING

Teach

▪ Explain that words can be classified, or grouped together, according to the way in which they are alike. For example, shoes, socks, and slippers are all things that are worn on the feet. Bushes, trees, and flowers are all things that are planted. Tell students that classifying words can help them see the connection between words. It can help them build their vocabulary.

▪ Write the following words on the board: *limber, elastic*, and *adaptable*. Discuss which word, *fragile, reliable*, or *flexible*, belongs with the group of words.

> **MODEL** To figure out the answer, I look to see what the words *limber*, *elastic*, and *adaptable* have in common. I see that they all describe something that can bend without breaking or that is able to change or take in new ideas. Of the three words, *flexible* goes best with these words.

Practice/Apply

▪ Assign the Classifying page. Have students familiarize themselves with the words in the word box before completing the page.

Follow-Up

▪ **Word Play** Have students make up questions such as the following for a partner to answer. Partners should be prepared to explain their answers.

- Which words might you use to talk about a vacation, *solitary, luxurious, linger*, or *transport*?
- Which words might you use to describe doing homework, *calculate, document, postpone*, or *strive*?

▪ **Informal Assessment** Provide Concept Circles (available online at **www.sadlier-oxford.com**) that incorporate some of the words students have learned so far. Have students replace the word that doesn't belong with a taught word that does. Then have them write a phrase that tells how the words in the circle are related.

Words that Describe a Deserted Building

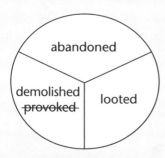

ANALOGIES

Teach

■ Explain that an analogy is a statement that shows a particular relationship between two pairs of words. To complete an analogy, you must know the meanings of all the words, and you must know how the words are related.

■ Tell students that analogies can be based on synonyms and antonyms. They can also show other relationships. For example:

- Object/Description: *sugar* is to *sweet* as *lemon* is to *sour*
- Part/Whole: *wrist* is to *arm* as *ankle* is to *leg*
- Object/Class: *poodle* is to *dog* as *woodpecker* is to *bird*
- Object/Function: *broom* is to *sweep* as *pencil* is to *write*

Have students suggest other word pairs for each type of relationship above.

■ Write the following on the board: "*monarch* is to *ruler* as *nomad* is to _____"
Model how to figure out an answer.

> **MODEL** Before I can figure out the answer, I need to think about how *monarch* is related to *ruler*. I see that the words are synonyms, so *nomad* and the missing word must also be synonyms. A logical choice would be *wanderer*. *Rover* and *roamer* would also be good choices.

Practice/Apply

■ Assign the two Analogies pages. Remind students to figure out the relationship between the words in the first pair before choosing the answer.

Follow-Up

■ **Writing** Have students record the analogies described above in their Vocabulary Notebook. Then, using these analogies as reference, have students work together to make up their own analogies. Tell them to use at least one taught word in each analogy and to be prepared to explain the relationship. If students have been adding to the word lists in their Vocabulary Notebooks, you may want to have them choose words from those lists.

BUILDING WITH LATIN AND GREEK ROOTS

Teach

■ Tell students that roots are word parts to which other parts, such as prefixes and suffixes, can be added. Explain that the root is the main part of the word. It is the part that carries the meaning of the word. Point out that the root of many English words comes from Latin; for example, the roots *port* and *spec* are Latin roots.

Latin Root *port*   (Cumulative Review I, Units 1–8, pp. 82–83)
■ On the board, write the word *portable*. Underline *port*, and explain that the Latin root *port* means "carry." Model how knowing the meaning of *port* can help you figure out the meaning of *portable* in the following: "Laptop computers are more *portable* than desktop models."

> **MODEL** The meaning of the root *port* gives me a clue to the meaning of the word *portable*. I also know that laptops are smaller and more compact than desktop computers. Using what I know about the size of computers and what I know about the meaning of the root *port*, I can figure out that something that is *portable* is easy to carry. I will check the definition of *portable* in a dictionary to see if I am right.

Latin Root *spec*   (Cumulative Review II, Units 9–16, pp. 154–155)
■ On the board, write the word *inspect*. Underline *spec*, and explain that the Latin root *spec* means "look." Model how knowing the meaning of the root *spec* can help you figure out the meaning of *inspect* in the following: "The foreman will *inspect* the repairs when the crew has completed its work."

> **MODEL** Using the information in the sentence and what I know about the root *spec*, I can figure out that *inspect* means "to look at something carefully in order to check it or find out what it is like." To check if this meaning is correct, I will look up *inspect* in a dictionary.

■ Point out that although knowing the meanings of roots can help us understand the meanings of English words, there is not always a clear connection between the Latin word and the English word. Explain that often this is because the meanings of some English words have changed over the centuries. Some words have become broader in meaning while others have become narrower.

Practice/Apply

- Before assigning the two Building with Latin and Greek Roots pages, discuss the word with the root in the blue box. Have students identify the root and then give the meaning of the word. Relate the meaning to the meaning of the root.

Follow-Up

Latin Root *port* (Cumulative Review I, Units 1–8, pp. 82–83)

- **Expanding Vocabulary** If students demonstrate an interest in roots, present the following with the Latin roots *sign* and *cred*:

Root	Meaning	Words
sign	mark	significant, insignia
cred	believe	credible, credit

Underline *sign* in *significant* and *insignia*, and explain that *sign* means "mark." Then underline *cred* in *credible* and *credit*, and explain that *cred* means "believe." Have students give the meaning of each of the four words. If a word is unfamiliar to them, have students look up the word in a dictionary. Encourage students to use each word in a sentence.

Latin Root *spec* (Cumulative Review II, Units 9–16, pp. 154–155)

- **Expanding Vocabulary** As they read, ask students to be on the alert for words with the roots they have learned, including the roots *sign* and *cred*. For each word, have them complete the following in their Vocabulary Notebook.

Root_____

Meaning_____

Word_____

Definition_____

Sentence_____

Be sure to review the words with students to make sure that each word is derived from one of the taught roots.

Answer Key to Level Blue Supplementary Testing Program
Form A (Cycle One)

UNIT 1
1. **c** temporary
2. **a** cancel
3. **d** solitary
4. **b** scuffle
5. **d** veteran
6. **d** reject
7. **c** document
8. blunder
9. continuous
10. fragile
11. reject
12. myth
13. distributed
14. **d** issue
15. **a** prove
16. **c** single
17. **b** error
18. **c** tale
19. **a** fight
20. **a** renew
21. **d** hardy
22. **b** rookie
23. **d** accept
24. **a** interrupted
25. **c** permanent

UNIT 2
1. **c** impressive
2. **a** strategy
3. **b** convert
4. **d** justify
5. **b** misleading
6. **a** assault
7. **d** Productive
8. dispute
9. villain
10. numerous
11. shrewd
12. abandoned
13. assault
14. **a** transformed
15. **b** sharp
16. **d** deceptive
17. **c** scheme
18. **b** striking
19. **a** defend
20. **b** defend
21. **a** idle
22. **d** agree

23. **a** occupy
24. **c** few
25. **b** hero

UNIT 3
1. **b** miniature
2. **d** postpone
3. **c** straggle
4. **a** consist
5. **d** obstacle
6. **d** haven
7. **c** bluff
8. monarch
9. cautious
10. treacherous
11. despised
12. vivid
13. bluff
14. **b** hurdles
15. **d** tiny
16. **a** delay
17. **a** wander
18. **d** hearty
19. **b** is made of
20. **a** daring
21. **b** trap
22. **d** faithful
23. **c** commoner
24. **b** adore
25. **d** dull

UNIT 4
1. **a** mishap
2. **d** aggressive
3. **b** hazy
4. **c** associate
5. **b** span
6. **a** linger
7. **d** Luxurious
8. glamour
9. deceive
10. flexible
11. emigrate
12. overwhelmed
13. linger
14. **a** bridge
15. **a** blunder
16. **d** relocate
17. **c** crush

18. **b** cheat
19. **d** beauty
20. **a** hurry
21. **d** timid
22. **b** rigid
23. **c** clear
24. **b** modest
25. **a** rival

MASTERY TEST I
(UNITS 1–4)
1. mishap
2. deceive
3. impressive
4. scuffle
5. obstacle
6. V
7. N
8. A
9. A
10. V
11. V
12. N
13. V
14. N
15. A
16. postpone
17. abandon
18. luxurious
19. bluff
20. distribute
21. document
22. misleading
23. productive
24. emigrate
25. consist

UNIT 5
1. **d** Blunt
2. **a** fatigue
3. **c** blemish
4. **b** transport
5. **c** persecute
6. **d** Hospitality
7. **a** conclude
8. capable
9. festive
10. detect
11. nomads
12. supreme
13. concluded
14. **d** haul
15. **a** wanderers
16. **c** spot
17. **b** torment

18. **d** defect
19. **c** greatest
20. **a** tactful
21. **d** begin
22. **a** hostility
23. **c** gloomy
24. **d** unqualified
25. **c** energy

UNIT 6
1. **a** provoke
2. **d** duplicates
3. **b** conceal
4. **b** capacity
5. **c** spurt
6. **b** civilian
7. **a** apparent
8. vast
9. accomplish
10. keen
11. withdrew
12. undoing
13. capacity
14. **d** downfall
15. **a** gift
16. **d** surge
17. **b** acute
18. **c** subtract
19. **c** achieve
20. **a** military
21. **c** tiny
22. **b** reveal
23. **d** original
24. **b** uncertain
25. **c** calm

UNIT 7
1. **c** jolt
2. **b** shrivel
3. **a** Senseless
4. **d** considerable
5. **c** deputy
6. **b** Industrious
7. **d** compose
8. calculate
9. rejoice
10. barrier
11. reliable
12. loot

13. compose
14. **d** rattled
15. **a** assistant
16. **c** settle
17. **b** untiring
18. **b** determine
19. **b** booty
20. **b** opening
21. **d** mourn
22. **c** swelling
23. **b** smart
24. **a** slight
25. **d** fickle

UNIT 8

1. **c** Mature
2. **a** demolish
3. **b** observant
4. **d** alternate
5. **c** feat
6. **a** enforce
7. **d** Energetic
8. strive
9. resigned
10. demolish
11. hearty
12. verdict
13. primary
14. **c** achievement
15. **a** struggle
16. **b** leave
17. **b** replacement
18. **d** ruling
19. **c** destroy
20. **a** idle
21. **d** secondary
22. **b** phony
23. **c** disregard
24. **a** unripe
25. **d** inattentive

MASTERY TEST II (UNITS 5–8)

1. capacity
2. provoke
3. mature
4. blunt
5. deputy

6. A
7. N
8. A
9. V
10. N
11. N
12. V
13. A
14. N
15. V
16. undoing
17. calculate
18. fatigue
19. duplicate
20. shrivel
21. supreme
22. enforce
23. demolish
24. withdraw
25. jolt

UNIT 9

1. **a** considerate
2. **d** humiliated
3. **c** downfall
4. **b** displace
5. **c** vicinity
6. **a** Improper
7. **c** cherish
8. identical
9. polled
10. brisk
11. estimated
12. soothe
13. downfall
14. **b** survey
15. **d** neighborhood
16. **a** treasure
17. **c** guess
18. **b** unsuitable
19. **d** uproot
20. **c** different
21. **a** thoughtless
22. **b** praise
23. **d** worsen
24. **c** sluggish
25. **a** triumph

UNIT 10

1. **b** abolish
2. **d** Thrifty
3. **c** dictator
4. **d** visual
5. **a** famine
6. **b** prey
7. **c** condemn

8. expands
9. descend
10. appeal
11. portable
12. brittle
13. condemn
14. **d** tyrant
15. **b** victim
16. **a** ban
17. **d** come down
18. **a** plea
19. **d** seeing
20. **c** applaud
21. **d** bendable
22. **a** immovable
23. **b** extravagant
24. **a** reduce
25. **c** plenty

UNIT 11

1. **b** security
2. **c** avalanche
3. **d** navigate
4. **a** selective
5. **a** ensure
6. **d** absurd
7. **c** Reasonable
8. plea
9. tart
10. classify
11. principle
12. nestle
13. avalanche
14. **a** cascade
15. **d** standards
16. **b** steer
17. **c** appeal
18. **d** catalog
19. **b** snuggle
20. **d** impractical
21. **a** risk
22. **c** sweet
23. **b** careless
24. **a** peril
25. **a** sensible

UNIT 12

1. **a** Appliances
2. **d** daze
3. **b** Migrant
4. **c** rotate

5. **d** flimsy
6. **c** confirm
7. **b** presentable
8. abuse
9. neutral
10. shred
11. gauge
12. pitiless
13. confirm
14. **a** assess
15. **c** stupor
16. **b** switch
17. **d** drifters
18. **c** check
19. **a** utensil
20. **b** shabby
21. **d** convincing
22. **c** opinionated
23. **a** merciful
24. **d** repair
25. **b** cherish

MASTERY TEST III (UNITS 9–12)

1. migrant
2. appliance
3. security
4. plea
5. brittle
6. V
7. N
8. A
9. N
10. V
11. V
12. N
13. V
14. V
15. A
16. improper
17. abolish
18. estimate
19. visual
20. pitiless
21. principle
22. downfall
23. selective
24. navigate
25. neutral

UNIT 13
1. **c** acquire
2. **a** sprawl
3. **b** widespread
4. **a** monotonous
5. **d** massacre
6. **c** latter
7. **b** exhibit
8. sanitary
9. exhibit
10. preserve
11. debate
12. foe
13. achievement
14. **d** slaughter
15. **a** lounge
16. **c** reveals
17. **b** clean
18. **d** sanctuary
19. **a** second
20. **c** failure
21. **b** comrade
22. **a** varied
23. **d** limited
24. **c** agreement
25. **b** lose

UNIT 14
1. **b** alibi
2. **a** discharge
3. **d** reign
4. **d** frank
5. **c** modify
6. **b** negative
7. **c** singular
8. confederate
9. swindle
10. pursue
11. economical
12. mutiny
13. negatives
14. **a** alter
15. **c** excuse
16. **d** cheat
17. **b** regime
18. **a** uprising
19. **d** chase
20. **c** hire
21. **d** plural
22. **a** favorable
23. **d** extravagant
24. **b** insincere
25. **c** enemy

UNIT 15
1. **d** complicate
2. **a** severe
3. **c** scorch
4. **b** trifle
5. **c** moral
6. **a** Courteous
7. **d** Universal
8. tragic
9. discomfort
10. eliminate
11. grieved
12. spectacle
13. universal
14. **b** blacken
15. **a** polite
16. **d** worldwide
17. **c** marvel
18. **b** remove
19. **a** trinket
20. **d** simplify
21. **b** wicked
22. **a** comical
23. **c** mild
24. **c** peace
25. **a** celebrate

UNIT 16
1. **d** assume
2. **b** rigid
3. **a** fertile
4. **a** mammoth
5. **c** peer
6. **d** rowdy
7. **b** endanger
8. safeguard
9. cram
10. fare
11. furnishes
12. trespassing
13. mammoth
14. **a** colleague
15. **c** threaten
16. **b** enormous
17. **d** suppose
18. **a** food
19. **d** intrude
20. **b** barren
21. **a** flexible
22. **d** threaten
23. **c** gentle
24. **a** withhold
25. **b** empty

MASTERY TEST IV (UNITS 13–16)
1. exhibit
2. sprawl
3. modify
4. assume
5. severe
6. V
7. N
8. A
9. A
10. N
11. V
12. N
13. V
14. N
15. A
16. negative
17. furnish
18. cram
19. sanitary
20. economical
21. preserve
22. complicate
23. safeguard
24. peer
25. eliminate

FINAL MASTERY TEST
1. hearty
2. pursue
3. universal
4. latter
5. aggressive
6. presentable
7. capable
8. rowdy
9. brittle
10. displace
11. fragile
12. no change: linger
13. alternate
14. soothe
15. absurd
16. achievement
17. singular
18. no change: fertile
19. abuse
20. keen
21. cherish
22. reign
23. flimsy
24. treacherous
25. prey
26. nestle
27. confirm
28. spectacle
29. **c** several
30. **a** obvious
31. **d** plead
32. **b** sensible
33. **a** obtain
34. **d** dreadful
35. **d** agreement
36. **a** fickle
37. **b** friend
38. **d** load
39. **a** climb
40. **b** impolite
41. **d**
42. **b**
43. **a**
44. **c**
45. **c**
46. **a**
47. **b**
48. **d**
49. **a**
50. **c**

UNIT 1
1. **b** blunder
2. **a** distribute
3. **c** document
4. **c** myth
5. **d** Fragile
6. **b** continuous
7. **d** temporary
8. veteran
9. scuffle
10. solitary
11. documents
12. cancel
13. reject
14. **a** brawl
15. **b** divide
16. **a** dismiss
17. **c** legend
18. **d** expert
19. **c** certificate
20. **d** sociable
21. **d** interrupted
22. **a** permanent
23. **a** success
24. **c** sturdy
25. **b** continue

UNIT 2
1. **b** villain
2. **d** abandon
3. **a** misleading
4. **b** convert
5. **d** strategy
6. **a** shrewd
7. **d** productive
8. justify
9. villain
10. assault
11. dispute
12. numerous
13. impressive
14. **b** attack
15. **c** several
16. **a** awesome
17. **c** change
18. **d** explain
19. **c** scheme
20. **d** true
21. **a** inactive

22. **c** foolish
23. **b** occupy
24. **b** agree with
25. **c** heroine

UNIT 3
1. **d** miniature
2. **c** monarch
3. **a** consist
4. **c** straggle
5. **b** treacherous
6. **a** Cautious
7. **b** haven
8. bluff
9. despises
10. vivid
11. postponed
12. obstacles
13. straggled
14. **a** trick
15. **c** is made of
16. **d** lively
17. **b** dangerous
18. **d** careful
19. **b** roam
20. **d** trap
21. **a** move up
22. **a** enormous
23. **b** help
24. **b** commoner
25. **c** adore

UNIT 4
1. **c** span
2. **c** aggressive
3. **b** associate
4. **d** overwhelm
5. **a** hazy
6. **d** mishap
7. **b** deceive
8. emigrate
9. glamour
10. flexible
11. linger
12. luxurious
13. aggressive
14. **b** astound
15. **a** mistake
16. **b** charm

17. **d** relocate
18. **a** fool
19. **c** distance
20. **c** unbendable
21. **d** precise
22. **a** hurry
23. **b** simple
24. **c** timid
25. **c** foe

MASTERY TEST I (UNITS 1–4)
1. misleadng
2. luxurious
3. solitary
4. myth
5. postpone
6. A
7. V
8. A
9. A
10. N
11. N
12. A
13. V
14. N
15. V
16. strategy
17. shrewd
18. treacherous
19. consist
20. flexible
21. temporary
22. justify
23. impressive
24. linger
25. reject

UNIT 5
1. **a** fatigue
2. **d** blemish
3. **b** blunt
4. **c** persecute
5. **d** hospitality
6. **a** festive
7. **d** transport
8. hospitality
9. nomad
10. supreme
11. detect
12. conclude
13. capable
14. **c** carry
15. **d** find

16. **b** sleepiness
17. **b** wanderers
18. **c** greatest
19. **d** flaw
20. **c** gloomy
21. **a** unfit
22. **a** begin
23. **c** hostility
24. **c** tactful
25. **a** comfort

UNIT 6
1. **b** civilian
2. **a** provoke
3. **c** accomplish
4. **b** keen
5. **c** withdraw
6. **d** apparent
7. **a** undoing
8. spurt
9. vast
10. undoing
11. duplicate
12. capacity
13. concealed
14. **a** room
15. **a** complete
16. **d** obvious
17. **d** remove
18. **c** spacious
19. **a** surge
20. **b** reveal
21. **b** original
22. **a** dull
23. **d** success
24. **c** military
25. **d** calm

UNIT 7
1. **c** senseless
2. **a** calculate
3. **c** deputy
4. **b** jolt
5. **c** loot
6. **d** barrier
7. **b** reliable
8. shriveled
9. rejoice
10. jolt
11. Industrious

12. compose
13. considerable
14. **a** booty
15. **b** figure
16. **c** assistant
17. **a** lurch
18. **b** invent
19. **d** active
20. **c** small
21. **a** grieve
22. **d** clever
23. **c** fickle
24. **a** expand
25. **d** opening

UNIT 8
1. **a** resign
2. **b** alternate
3. **a** mature
4. **a** strive
5. **c** verdict
6. **d** demolish
7. **c** primary
8. energetic
9. strive
10. enforce
11. observant
12. feat
13. hearty
14. **c** rotate
15. **a** ruling
16. **b** quit
17. **c** attempt
18. **a** achievement
19. **c** main
20. **a** disregard
21. **a** built
22. **a** phony
23. **d** unripe
24. **c** careless
25. **a** lazy

MASTERY TEST II (UNITS 5–8)
1. conceal
2. spurt
3. compose
4. observant
5. blemish

6. V
7. V
8. A
9. N
10. A

11. A
12. V
13. A
14. N
15. N

16. senseless
17. reliable
18. energetic
19. resign
20. festive
21. provoke
22. vast
23. feat
24. mature
25. transport

UNIT 9
1. **d** vicinity
2. **b** poll
3. **c** estimate
4. **b** Brisk
5. **c** soothe
6. **d** cherish
7. **a** Improper
8. identical
9. considerate
10. vicinity
11. humiliated
12. downfall
13. displaced
14. **c** guess
15. **c** survey
16. **a** quiet
17. **c** fresh
18. **b** honor
19. **a** neighborhood
20. **d** thoughtless
21. **c** settle
22. **b** praise
23. **a** polite
24. **c** different
25. **d** success

UNIT 10
1. **c** dictator
2. **b** thrifty
3. **c** visual
4. **a** expand
5. **c** appeal
6. **b** prey
7. **a** condemn

8. visual
9. Portable
10. descend
11. abolish
12. brittle
13. famine
14. **b** visible
15. **a** tyrant
16. **b** come down
17. **d** charm
18. **c** frugal
19. **a** feed
20. **d** immovable
21. **a** bendable
22. **a** praise
23. **b** reduce
24. **c** feast
25. **b** establish

UNIT 11
1. **d** avalanche
2. **a** nestle
3. **d** classify
4. **c** plea
5. **b** principles
6. **c** absurd
7. **d** realistic
8. ensure
9. navigate
10. security
11. selective
12. tart
13. avalanche
14. **b** catalog
15. **a** steer
16. **c** appeal
17. **a** standards
18. **d** snuggle
19. **b** landslide
20. **d** endanger
21. **a** gentle
22. **c** impractical
23. **c** careless
24. **d** danger
25. **b** sensible

UNIT 12
1. **b** rotate
2. **c** migrant
3. **a** appliance
4. **c** confirm

5. **b** daze
6. **c** flimsy
7. **a** abuse
8. gauge
9. neutral
10. pitiless
11. presentable
12. shred
13. rotates
14. **d** gadget
15. **a** trance
16. **d** assess
17. **c** drifters
18. **a** strip
19. **c** alternate
20. **b** care
21. **a** cancel
22. **c** opinionated
23. **b** kindhearted
24. **a** sturdy
25. **d** shabby

MASTERY TEST III (UNITS 9–12)
1. neutral
2. tart
3. senseless
4. condemn
5. cherish

6. V
7. V
8. A
9. N
10. N

11. V
12. V
13. A
14. A
15. N

16. considerate
17. descend
18. appeal
19. plea
20. shred
21. brisk
22. humiliate
23. dictator
24. avalanche
25. confirm

UNIT 13
1. **b** massacre
2. **a** sprawl
3. **a** achievement
4. **c** widespread
5. **d** acquire

6. **c** sanitary
7. **b** debate
8. preserve
9. sprawl
10. exhibit
11. monotonous
12. foe
13. latter
14. **d** far-reaching
15. **c** slaughter
16. **b** clean
17. **a** triumphs
18. **b** lounge
19. **c** refuge
20. **c** agree
21. **a** hide
22. **c** lively
23. **b** first
24. **a** friend
25. **d** lose

UNIT 14

1. **c** modify
2. **b** alibi
3. **d** reign
4. **b** swindle
5. **c** economical
6. **a** pursue
7. **d** singular
8. Confederate
9. negative
10. swindle
11. mutiny
12. discharged
13. frank
14. **d** rule
15. **a** cheat
16. **c** excuse
17. **a** revise
18. **d** ally
19. **c** unusual
20. **b** flee
21. **a** appoint
22. **d** insincere
23. **c** wasteful
24. **d** positive
25. **a** obey

UNIT 15

1. **c** spectacle
2. **d** scorch

3. **c** universal
4. **b** complicate
5. **a** trifle
6. **b** Severe
7. **c** discomfort
8. courteous
9. tragic
10. eliminate
11. moral
12. grieved
13. spectacles
14. **b** general
15. **c** singe
16. **d** stern
17. **a** disastrous
18. **b** knickknacks
19. **c** show
20. **d** rude
21. **b** preserve
22. **a** peace
23. **b** rejoice
24. **d** wicked
25. **b** simplify

UNIT 16

1. **b** fare
2. **a** Peer
3. **b** trespass
4. **d** rowdy
5. **c** safeguard
6. **a** assume
7. **d** rigid
8. mammoth
9. cram
10. furnishes
11. endangers
12. fertile
13. trespass
14. **c** intrude
15. **b** food
16. **b** colleagues
17. **c** accept
18. **a** protect
19. **b** stuff
20. **a** protect
21. **c** barren
22. **d** small
23. **b** take
24. **a** flexible
25. **c** quiet

MASTERY TEST IV (UNITS 13–16)

1. acquire
2. widespread
3. cram
4. grieve
5. frank
6. V
7. V
8. A
9. A
10. A
11. N
12. N
13. V
14. N
15. V
16. assume
17. rigid
18. moral
19. achievement
20. modify
21. singular
22. swindle
23. discomfort
24. fertile
25. mammoth

FINAL MASTERY TEST

1. detect
2. dispute
3. miniature
4. mishap
5. abandon
6. withdraw
7. vicinity
8. portable
9. selective
10. migrant
11. endanger
12. trespass
13. no change: universal
14. trifle
15. pursue
16. no change: economical
17. monotonous
18. sprawl
19. rotate
20. appliance
21. considerable
22. hearty
23. navigate
24. estimate
25. overwhelm
26. capable
27. demolish

28. misleading
29. **b** complete
30. **c** jerk
31. **d** breakable
32. **a** comfort
33. **d** lone
34. **a** hurdle
35. **c** barren
36. **d** celebrate
37. **d** appoint
38. **c** defeat
39. **a** deny
40. **b** sweet
41. **b**
42. **d**
43. **d**
44. **a**
45. **c**
46. **b**
47. **a**
48. **c**
49. **a**
50. **c**

NOTES

Vocabulary Workshop
New Edition

Level Blue

Jerome Shostak

Consultants

Virginia M. Russell
Director of Clinical Experiences
Hunter College, School of Education
New York, NY

Elaine M. Czarnecki
Literacy Consultant
Annapolis, MD

Diane Flora
Reading Specialist
Indianapolis, IN

Sadlier-Oxford
A Division of William H. Sadlier, Inc.

Vocabulary Workshop
New Edition

Reviewers

The publisher wishes to thank the following teachers for their thorough review and thoughtful comments on portions of the series prior to publication.

Sharon West
Fifth Grade Teacher
Tallahassee, FL

Patty Bowman
Fifth Grade Teacher
Plano, TX

Debbie Dantin
Fifth Grade Teacher
Marrero, LA

Photo Credits
Christie's Images Ltd: 13.
Corbis/Bettmann: 51, 63, 142; Michael Busselle: 57; Hulton-Deutsch Collection: 103.

Everett Collection: 19.

Getty Images/Hulton Archive: 25, 70; Stone/Lorne Resnick: 45; Photodisc: 83; Stone/Lornetz Gullachsen: 85; Stone/Bruce Forster: 97; National Geographic/Walter Meayers Edwards: 110; Stone/Michael Rosenfeld: 117; Stone/Gary Holscher: 135; Reportage/Ezra Shaw: 155.

The Granger Collection: *New York*: 38.

PunchStock/Panoramic Images: 129.

retrofile.com/C.P. Cushing: 91.

robertstock.com: 31.

Illustrator
Daryl Stevens: 43, 75, 115, 147.

Printed in the United States of America.
ISBN: 0-8215-0365-0
123456789/09 08 07 06 05

CONTENTS

FOREWORD

For over half a century Vocabulary Workshop has proven a highly successful tool for promoting and guiding systematic vocabulary growth. Level Blue is meant both to help younger students *increase* their vocabulary and to *improve* their vocabulary skills. It has also been designed to help prepare students for vocabulary-related items found in standardized tests.

This New Edition of Vocabulary Workshop Level Blue maintains the core of the original edition—the Word List and the 16 Units—and introduces in the restructured Reviews and Cumulative Reviews several important new features:

- **Vocabulary for Comprehension** is modeled on the reading sections of standardized tests, and, as in those tests, presents reading comprehension questions, including vocabulary-related ones, based on a reading passage. Representing a variety of genres—both fiction and nonfiction—these reading passages offer students practice with many types of text.

- **Grammar in Context** is linked to the Vocabulary for Comprehension passage, referring to a grammar, usage, or mechanics skill illustrated in that passage. Grammar in Context is designed to give students instruction and practice in the grammar skills commonly assessed on standardized tests and, at the same time, to improve their writing by giving students a stronger footing in the conventions of standard English.

- **Completing the Idea** gives students a prompt, in the form of a sentence-starter that contains a taught word, and invites them to complete a thought in any way that they like. This exercise offers students the opportunity to express themselves, and teachers a way of assessing how well their students have mastered the meaning and usage of the taught words.

- **Write Your Own** provides students an opportunity to write an original sentence that correctly uses one of the taught words and that illustrates the grammar skill discussed in the foregoing Grammar in Context exercise.

- **Building with Latin and Greek Roots** shows students how the knowledge of a word stemming from a Latin or Greek root can help them uncover the meaning of other words containing that same root.

Also new to this edition are **Interactive Online Activities** that extend and enrich the instruction and practice contained in the student text. These online activities cover all 192 taught words with engaging word games and crossword puzzles. Access to these free activities is available at www.sadlier-oxford.com.

THE VOCABULARY OF VOCABULARY

English has a large group of special terms to describe how words are used and how they are related to one another. These terms make up what we might call the "vocabulary of vocabulary." Learning to understand and use the vocabulary of vocabulary will help you to get better results in your vocabulary-building program.

Part of Speech

Every word in English plays some role in the language. What that role is determines how a word is classified grammatically. These classifications are called "parts of speech." In English there are eight parts of speech: nouns, pronouns, verbs, adjectives, adverbs, prepositions, conjunctions, and interjections. All of the words introduced in this book are nouns (abbreviated *n.*), verbs (*v.*), or adjectives (*adj.*).

A **noun** names a person, place, or thing. *Uncle, home,* and *food* are nouns. So are *Lincoln, Chicago,* and *Superbowl.* Nouns also name things such as ideas and feelings; for example, *justice, space,* and *anger* are nouns.

Verbs express action or a state of being. *Go, be, live, tell, write, speak, listen, leave, arrive,* and *behave* are verbs.

Adjectives describe or give information about nouns or other adjectives. *Happy, sad, quick, slow, big, little, black, white, first,* and *last* are adjectives.

Many English words act as more than one part of speech. The word *bend,* for example, can be a verb or a noun. Its part of speech depends upon the way it is used.

NOUN: We came to a bend in the river. [*bend* names a thing]

VERB: The wind made the trees bend. [*bend* expresses an action]

EXERCISES   For each sentence, circle the choice that identifies the part of speech of the word in **boldface**.

1. My brother is a **fast** runner.
   a. noun   b. verb   (c.) adjective

2. Let's **work** together to solve the problem.
   a. noun   (b.) verb   c. adjective

3. I have a lot of **work** to do this weekend.
   (a.) noun   b. verb   c. adjective

4. I'm wearing a **new** pair of socks.
   a. noun   b. verb   (c.) adjective

5. There were a lot of happy **faces** in the crowd.
   (a.) noun   b. verb   c. adjective

6. The front of the house **faces** East.
   a. noun   (b.) verb   c. adjective

Synonyms and Antonyms

Synonyms

A synonym is a word that means *the same* or *nearly the same* as another word.

EXAMPLES   gift — present   smart — clever

cry — weep   joy — happiness

thin — skinny   begin — start

EXERCISES   For each of the following groups, circle the choice that is most nearly the **same** in meaning as the word in **boldface**.

1. **silent**	2. **jog**	3. **law**	4. **tidy**
a. noisy	a. crawl	(a.) rule	a. messy
b. kind	(b.) trot	b. school	b. small
c. playful	c. laugh	c. jail	c. new
(d.) quiet	d. stop	d. sheriff	(d.) neat

Antonyms

An antonym is a word that is *opposite* or *nearly opposite* in meaning to another word.

EXAMPLES   grow — shrink   huge — tiny

crowded — empty   victory — defeat

friend — enemy   hide — show

EXERCISES   For each of the following groups, circle the choice that is most nearly **opposite** in meaning to the word in **boldface**.

1. **simple**	2. **wealth**	3. **punish**	4. **healthy**
a. easy	a. fame	(a.) reward	a. bossy
(b.) difficult	b. success	b. trust	b. messy
c. cheap	(c.) poverty	c. trick	c. sturdy
d. boring	d. taxes	d. remember	(d.) sickly

Context Clues

When you turn to the "Completing the Sentence" and "Vocabulary for Comprehension" exercises in this book, look for clues built into the passages to guide you to the correct answers. There are three basic types of clues.

Restatement Clues   A restatement clue gives a *definition of,* or a *synonym for,* a missing word.

EXAMPLE   The climbers slowly made their way to the <u>top of the mountain</u> until at last they reached its very _____.

a. bottom   b. slope   c. peak   d. range

Contrast Clues   A contrast clue gives an *antonym for,* or a phrase meaning *the opposite of,* a missing word.

EXAMPLE   The weather was <u>mild</u> at the foot of the mountain, but the conditions at the top were _____.

a. nice   b. harsh   c. friendly   d. dry

Situational Clues   Sometimes the situation itself, as it is outlined in the sentence or passage, suggests the word that is missing but does not state the meaning directly.

EXAMPLE   After the <u>long and dangerous</u> return from the top of the mountain, the climbers were very _____.

a. bored   b. weary   c. fresh   d. guilty

To figure out which word is missing from the sentence, ask yourself this question: How would the climbers feel after a "long and dangerous" journey? Would they feel bored? Weary? Fresh? Guilty?

EXERCISES   Use context clues to choose the word that best completes each of the following sentences.

1. Why argue over such silly matters when we have so many _____ problems to deal with?
   a. little   b. foolish   c. serious   d. unimportant

2. We will have to _____ for hours to get rid of all the grime.
   a. play   b. read   c. sing   d. scrub

3. The noise in the crowded gym was so great that we could barely make ourselves heard above the _____.
   a. racket   b. score   c. chairs   d. clock

Analogies

An **analogy** is a comparison. For example, we can make an analogy, or comparison, between a computer and a human brain.

In this book, you will be asked to find the relationship between two words. Then, to show that you understand that relationship, you will be asked to choose another pair of words that shows the same relationship.

EXAMPLES

1. **close** is to **open** as

   a. dance is to swim

   b. hold is to pinch

   c. stop is to go

   d. talk is to chat

2. **push** is to **shove** as

   a. grab is to release

   b. giggle is to laugh

   c. hope is to try

   d. watch is to listen

In the first example, note that *close* and *open* are **antonyms**; they are opposite in meaning. Of the four choices given, which pair is made up of words that are also antonyms, or opposite in meaning? The answer, of course, is *c, stop is to go*.

In the second example, note that *push* and *shove* are **synonyms**; they have nearly the same meaning. Of the four choices given, which pair is made up of words that are also synonyms, or nearly the same in meaning? The answer is *b, giggle is to laugh*.

There are many other kinds of analogies besides ones based on synonyms and antonyms. For each of the exercises that follow, first study carefully the pair of words in **boldface**. Then, when you have figured out the relationship between the two words, look for another pair that has the same relationship. Circle the item that best completes the analogy, and then write the relationship on the lines provided.

3. **steel** is to **metal** as

   a. oak is to wood

   b. pencil is to pen

   c. glass is to bottle

   d. jewel is to diamond

Relationship: _Steel_ is a type of _metal_; _oak_ is a type of _wood._

4. **petal** is to **flower** as

   a. baseball is to hockey

   b. cover is to magazine

   c. letter is to note

   d. branch is to tree

Relationship: A _petal_ is part of a _flower_; a _branch_ is part of a _tree._

5. **kitten** is to **cat** as

   a. chick is to egg

   b. horse is to colt

   c. puppy is to dog

   d. cub is to den

Relationship: A _kitten_ is a baby _cat_; a _puppy_ is a baby _dog._

PRONUNCIATION KEY

The pronunciation is given for every basic word introduced in this book. The symbols, which are shown below, are similar to those that appear in most standard dictionaries. The author has consulted a large number of dictionaries for this purpose but has relied primarily on *Webster's Third New International Dictionary* and *The Random House Dictionary of the English Language (Unabridged)*.

Of course, there are many English words, including some that appear in this book, for which two (or more) pronunciations are commonly accepted. In virtually all cases where such words occur in this book, just one pronunciation is given. Exceptions to this rule are made, however, in cases when the pronunciation of a word changes according to its part of speech. For example, as a noun the word *object* is pronounced **äb′ jekt**; as a verb it is pronounced **əb jekt′**. These relatively simple pronunciation guides should be readily usable by students. It should be emphasized, however, that the best way to learn the pronunciation of a word is to listen to and imitate an educated speaker.

Vowels	ā	lake	e	stress	u	rug
	a	mat	ī	knife	ü	boot, new
	å	care	i	sit	u̇	foot, pull
	ä	bark, bottle	ō	flow	ə	ago, broken
	au̇	doubt	ô	all, cord	ûr	herd, bird,
	ē	beat, wordy	oi	oil		purse

Consonants	ch	child, lecture	s	cellar	wh	what
	g	give	sh	shun	y	yell
	j	gentle, bridge	th	thank	z	is
	ŋ	sing	t̶h	those	zh	measure

All other consonants are sounded as in the alphabet.

Stress	The accent mark *follows* the syllable receiving the major stress: en rich′.

 **Diagnostic Test**

*For each of the following items, circle the letter for the word or phrase that best expresses the meaning of the word in **boldface** in the introductory phrase.*

Example
a **frisky** puppy
a. wet   (b.) playful   c. sick   d. little

---

1. a **fragile** set of crystal glasses
   a. shiny   b. beautiful   c. matched   (d.) delicate

2. read about the **dispute**
   a. agreement   (b.) argument   c. election   d. discovery

3. **bluffed** a throw to first base
   a. caught   b. dropped   c. blocked   (d.) faked

4. painted in **vivid** colors
   (a.) brilliant   b. matching   c. contrasting   d. dull

5. a **span** of ninety feet
   a. ditch   (b.) length   c. road   d. depth

6. **lingered** at a party
   a. left   b. entertained   c. danced   (d.) stayed

7. lived like **nomads**
   a. athletes   (b.) wanderers   c. criminals   d. farmers

8. a **festive** mood
   a. sad   b. angry   c. generous   (d.) happy

9. a **keen** mind
   a. silly   b. troubled   (c.) sharp   d. dull

10. **composed** beautiful songs
    a. sang   (b.) wrote   c. played   d. listened to

11. a very **reliable** mechanic
    (a.) trustworthy   b. skilled   c. talkative   d. cheerful

12. wrote about her **feats**
    a. poems   b. relatives   (c.) deeds   d. shoes

13. the **primary** reason
    a. only   (b.) main   c. secret   d. wrong

14. **cherish** your friends
    a. argue with   b. forget   c. visit   (d.) treasure

15. made an **improper** turn
    (a.) wrong   b. left   c. unnecessary   d. sudden

16. survived a **famine**
    a. lack of shelter   (b.) lack of food   c. lack of news   d. lack of taste

17. **appealed** for volunteers
    a. voted   b. telephoned   (c.) asked   d. paid

18. an important **principle**
    a. act   b. goal   c. teacher   (d.) rule

19. a totally **absurd** idea
    a. interesting   (b.) foolish   c. sensible   d. confusing

20. **shreds** of paper
    (a.) bits   b. piles   c. pads   d. boxes

21. a **pitiless** dictator
    a. friendless   b. powerful   c. cheerful   (d.) heartless

22. surrounded by many **foes**
    a. deer   b. friends   (c.) enemies   d. neighbors

23. **pursued** the runaway horse
    (a.) chased   b. rode   c. saddled   d. fed

24. a **universal** problem
    (a.) worldwide   b. local   c. recent   d. temporary

25. enjoyed special holiday **fare**
    a. prayers   b. games   c. music   (d.) food and drink

Definitions

Study the spelling, pronunciation, part of speech, and definition given for each of the words below. Write the word in the blank space in the sentence that follows. Then read the synonyms and antonyms.

1. **blunder**
   (blun′ dər)

   (v.) to make a foolish or careless mistake; to move clumsily and carelessly
   I saw the hiker _____ blunder _____ through the woods.

   (n.) a serious or thoughtless mistake
   I was terribly embarrassed by my _____ blunder _____.

   SYNONYMS: (v.) to err, foul up, bungle, goof; (n.) an error, blooper
   ANTONYMS: (v.) to triumph, succeed; (n.) a success, hit

2. **cancel**
   (kan′ səl)

   (v.) to call off or do away with; to cross out with lines or other marks to show that something cannot be used again
   Maybe the principal will _____ cancel _____ classes if it continues to snow.

   SYNONYMS: to stop, discontinue, drop, repeal, revoke
   ANTONYMS: to renew, continue, extend, maintain

3. **continuous**
   (kən tin′ yü əs)

   (adj.) going on without a stop or break
   _____ Continuous _____ TV coverage began shortly after news of the disaster broke.

   SYNONYMS: ongoing, endless, ceaseless, unbroken, constant, perpetual
   ANTONYMS: broken, discontinuous, interrupted

4. **distribute**
   (di stri′ byüt)

   (v.) to give out in shares; to scatter or spread
   Our class will _____ distribute _____ leaflets announcing the school's fund-raising drive.

   SYNONYMS: to divide, share, deal, issue
   ANTONYMS: to gather, collect, hold

5. **document**
   (dä′ kyə ment)

   (n.) a written or printed record that gives information or proof
   The librarian found the old _____ document _____ between the pages of a book.

   (v.) to give written or printed proof; to support with evidence
   Writers often _____ document _____ their sources.

   SYNONYMS: (n.) a certificate, deed; (v.) to prove, establish

6. **fragile**
   (fra′ jəl)

   (adj.) easily broken or damaged, requiring special handling or care
   The _____ fragile _____ antique was carefully packed to protect it during shipment.

   SYNONYMS: weak, frail, breakable, delicate, brittle, flimsy
   ANTONYMS: sturdy, hardy, strong, rugged, tough

 For vocabulary games and activities, visit **www.sadlier-oxford.com**.

The Greek god Zeus, shown here in a Roman sculpture, is the subject of many ancient **myths** (word 7).

7. **myth**
(mi~~th~~)

(n.) an old story that explains why something is or how it came to be; something imaginary

The play is based on an ancient Greek _____myth_____ .

SYNONYMS: a legend, fable, tale, fantasy, fairy tale
ANTONYM: a fact

8. **reject**
(ri jekt')

(v.) to refuse to accept, agree to, believe, or use

Why did you _____reject_____ *the offer?*

SYNONYMS: to deny, discard, junk, scrap, decline, dismiss
ANTONYMS: to take, accept, receive, welcome

9. **scuffle**
(sku' fəl)

(v.) to fight or struggle closely with

A witness saw the two men _____scuffle_____ *in an alley.*

(n.) fight or struggle

Police officers were called in to break up the _____scuffle_____ .

SYNONYMS: (v.) to tussle, roughhouse, battle, brawl; (n.) a fistfight, clash

10. **solitary**
(sä' lə ter ē)

(adj.) living or being alone; being the only one

The old man led a _____solitary_____ *life.*

SYNONYMS: single, sole, lone
ANTONYMS: sociable; several, many, numerous

11. **temporary**
(tem' pə rer ē)

(adj.) lasting or used for a limited time

A blow to the head can cause a _____temporary_____ *loss of memory.*

SYNONYMS: short-term, passing, brief, momentary
ANTONYMS: lasting, long-lived, permanent

12. **veteran**
(ve' tə rən)

(n.) a person who has served in the armed forces; a person who has a lot of experience

The President spoke to a group of combat _____veterans_____ .

(adj.) having much experience in some job or field, seasoned

In her next movie, the actress will play a _____veteran_____ *reporter.*

SYNONYMS: (adj.) expert, professional, experienced, skilled, accomplished
ANTONYMS: (n.) a beginner, newcomer, novice, rookie

13

Match the Meaning

For each item below, choose the word whose meaning is suggested by the clue given. Then write the word in the space provided.

1. A roommate you have for only a month is a _____temporary_____ one.
   a. continuous   b. temporary   c. fragile   d. solitary

2. A black eye might be the result of a _____scuffle_____.
   a. scuffle   b. myth   c. veteran   d. blunder

3. To _____document_____ your age you might show a birth certificate or a driver's license.
   a. distribute   b. document   c. cancel   d. reject

4. A person who lives alone in the woods might be described as _____solitary_____.
   a. continuous   b. solitary   c. temporary   d. fragile

5. The idea that you will get warts from touching a frog is a _____myth_____.
   a. blunder   b. document   c. scuffle   d. myth

6. If I make a serious mistake, I commit a _____blunder_____.
   a. scuffle   b. document   c. myth   d. blunder

7. A box containing an item that can be broken easily might be stamped "_____fragile_____."
   a. solitary   b. temporary   c. fragile   d. continuous

8. A charity might _____distribute_____ food to the homeless.
   a. reject   b. cancel   c. scuffle   d. distribute

9. Something that goes on without stopping is _____continuous_____.
   a. continuous   b. temporary   c. solitary   d. fragile

10. To refuse a gift is to _____reject_____ it.
    a. cancel   b. scuffle   c. distribute   d. reject

11. A person who has a lot of experience at something is a _____veteran_____.
    a. blunder   b. myth   c. document   d. veteran

12. If I call off a party, I _____cancel_____ it.
    a. reject   b. blunder   c. cancel   d. scuffle

Synonyms

*For each item below, choose the word that is most nearly the **same** in meaning as the word or phrase in **boldface**. Then write your choice on the line provided.*

1. a **constant** flow of traffic
   a. fragile   b. temporary   c. continuous   d. veteran   _____ continuous _____

2. tried to hide the **blooper**
   a. document   b. myth   c. blunder   d. scuffle   _____ blunder _____

3. not a **single** cent
   a. temporary   b. fragile   c. solitary   d. veteran   _____ solitary _____

4. witnessed the **fight**
   a. myth   b. blunder   c. document   d. scuffle   _____ scuffle _____

5. very important **records**
   a. veterans   b. documents   c. myths   d. blunders   _____ documents _____

6. a collection of ancient **stories**
   a. documents   b. myths   c. veterans   d. blunders   _____ myths _____

Antonyms

*For each item below, choose the word that is most nearly **opposite** in meaning to the word or phrase in **boldface**. Then write your choice on the line provided.*

1. **renew** my subscription
   a. cancel   b. blunder   c. scuffle   d. distribute   _____ cancel _____

2. **accept** the marriage proposal
   a. scuffle   b. reject   c. blunder   d. distribute   _____ reject _____

3. a **novice** mountain climber
   a. temporary   b. fragile   c. continuous   d. veteran   _____ veteran _____

4. **collect** the homework sheets
   a. reject   b. document   c. distribute   d. cancel   _____ distribute _____

5. a **sturdy** device
   a. temporary   b. solitary   c. veteran   d. fragile   _____ fragile _____

6. a **permanent** filling
   a. veteran   b. continuous   c. temporary   d. solitary   _____ temporary _____

Completing the Sentence

From the list of words on pages 12–13, choose the one that best completes each item below. Then write the word in the space provided. (You may have to change the word's ending.)

A VISIT TO A MUSEUM

■ Our class visited the museum on the last day of a(n) _____**temporary**_____ exhibit of ancient Greek vases. The vases had been on display for three months and were going to be returned to the European museums that had lent them.

■ Some of the vases were more than 2,000 years old. Because they were so old and _____**fragile**_____, we weren't allowed to touch them.

■ Security guards kept visitors a few feet from the display cases, so there was no chance that someone could _____**blunder**_____ into them.

■ The guide told us that the pictures painted on some of the vases were not of real people but characters from legends and _____**myths**_____.

■ One picture showed a(n) _____**solitary**_____ warrior fighting off a band of attackers. Our guide explained that the lone fighter was the Greek warrior Achilles and that his attackers were soldiers of Troy.

A FAMOUS DECLARATION

■ In refusing to accept English rule, the writers of the Declaration of Independence _____**rejected**_____ the claim that Parliament had sovereignty, or lawful power, over the American colonies.

■ Those who supported the cause of American independence quickly printed and _____**distributed**_____ copies of the Declaration throughout the thirteen colonies.

■ The original _____**document**_____, one of America's historic treasures, is now on view at the National Archives building in Washington, D.C.

ON THE SOCCER FIELD

■ Two days of _____**continuous**_____ rain had turned the soccer field into a sea of mud and threatened to spoil the opening game of the season.

■ Before the game began, a _____**scuffle**_____ broke out in the stands when a few home-team fans came to blows with those rooting for the visiting team.

■ The referee threatened to _____**cancel**_____ the game and send all of the fans home if order was not restored.

■ Only when a handful of popular _____**veterans**_____ from both teams asked the fans to behave themselves did they finally settle down and let the game get under way.

*Circle the letter next to the word or expression that best completes the sentence or answers the question. Pay special attention to the word in **boldface**.*

1. A person might emerge from a **scuffle**
   a. with spaghetti and meatballs
   b. with scrapes and bruises
   c. with dollars and cents
   d. with hugs and kisses

2. Someone who has **blundered** would
   a. feel embarrassed
   b. be confident
   c. feel proud
   d. be rewarded

3. A **solitary** tree would probably
   a. have needles
   b. be chopped down
   c. change color in the fall
   d. stand alone

4. A **continuous** loud noise might
   a. be hard to hear
   b. stop and start
   c. be soothing
   d. be annoying

5. Which of the following is a **document**?
   a. an old friend
   b. a telephone call
   c. a marriage license
   d. a good meal

6. If I **cancel** my piano lesson,
   a. I don't go
   b. I play very well
   c. I repair the piano
   d. I arrive late

7. A **temporary** problem is one that
   a. lasts a long time
   b. goes away
   c. no one can solve
   d. anyone can solve

8. In a **veteran's** closet you might find
   a. a skateboard
   b. a party dress
   c. a box of marbles
   d. an old uniform

9. When a teacher **distributes** a test
   a. he or she grades it
   b. he or she loses it
   c. he or she passes it out
   d. he or she collects it

10. Which of the following is usually **fragile**?
    a. a hammer
    b. a pair of scissors
    c. a lightbulb
    d. a padlock

11. Someone who has been **rejected**
    a. might feel hurt
    b. might feel happy
    c. might get lost
    d. might get a cold

12. Which is a creature of **myth**?
    a. a rabbit
    b. a giraffe
    c. a duck
    d. a dragon

Definitions

Study the spelling, pronunciation, part of speech, and definition given for each of the words below. Write the word in the blank space in the sentence that follows. Then read the synonyms and antonyms.

1. **abandon**
   (ə ban' dən)

   (v.) to give up on completely; to leave with no intention of returning
   The captain gave the order to _____abandon_____ ship.

   SYNONYMS: to desert, forsake, cease, surrender
   ANTONYMS: to continue, stay, remain, occupy

2. **assault**
   (ə sôlt')

   (n.) a violent attack
   The victim was seriously injured in the _____assault_____.
   (v.) to attack violently or suddenly
   Dad dared us to _____assault_____ his snow fort.

   SYNONYMS: (n.) an invasion, raid, mugging, beating; (v.) to besiege, storm
   ANTONYMS: (v.) to protect, defend, resist

3. **convert**
   (v., kən vûrt';
   n., kän' vûrt)

   (v.) to change from one form to another
   A drop in temperature to 32° F will _____convert_____ water to ice.
   (n.) a person who has changed from one opinion, belief, or religion to another
   The new _____convert_____ was introduced to the congregation.

   SYNONYMS: (v.) to transform, turn, alter, switch
   ANTONYMS: (v.) to maintain, conserve, remain

4. **dispute**
   (di spyüt')

   (v.) to argue, debate, quarrel over; to question or doubt the truth of
   The committee members did not _____dispute_____ the merits of the bill.
   (n.) an argument, quarrel, debate
   Why not try to resolve the _____dispute_____ peacefully?

   SYNONYMS: (v.) to differ, disagree; contest, challenge; (n.) a conflict, disagreement, controversy
   ANTONYMS: (v.) to agree, harmonize; (n.) an agreement, understanding, accord

5. **impressive**
   (im pre' siv)

   (adj.) having a strong effect, commanding attention
   The skater gave an _____impressive_____ performance.

   SYNONYMS: memorable, striking, stirring, thrilling, awesome, splendid
   ANTONYMS: inferior, mediocre

6. **justify**
   (jus' tə fī)

   (v.) to show to be fair or right; to give good reasons for
   Be prepared to _____justify_____ your behavior.

   SYNONYMS: to defend, explain, support, excuse
   ANTONYMS: to convict, blame, accuse

Internet For vocabulary games and activities, visit www.sadlier-oxford.com.

In old movies the **villain** (word 12) often wore a black hat.

7. **misleading**
(mis lē′ diŋ)

(adj.) tending to give a wrong idea, often on purpose
The lawyer called the statement _____misleading_____.

SYNONYMS: deceptive, false, tricky, inaccurate
ANTONYMS: direct, honest, true, accurate, straightforward

8. **numerous**
(nüm′ rəs)

(adj.) many or very many
_____Numerous_____ aunts and uncles came to our family reunion.

SYNONYMS: several, plenty, plentiful
ANTONYM: few

9. **productive**
(prə duk′ tiv)

(adj.) making or capable of making large amounts of; giving good results
With care it may become a _____productive_____ orchard.

SYNONYMS: energetic, effective, fruitful, efficient, worthwhile
ANTONYMS: unproductive, idle, useless, inactive

10. **shrewd**
(shrüd)

(adj.) showing clever judgment and practical understanding
My aunt is a _____shrewd_____ businesswoman.

SYNONYMS: artful, wise, sharp, crafty, wily, cunning
ANTONYMS: slow, stupid, dull-witted

11. **strategy**
(stra′ tə jē)

(n.) a carefully made plan or plot; a plan of military operations
Our teacher suggested a test-taking _____strategy_____.

SYNONYMS: an approach, design, method, scheme

12. **villain**
(vi′ lən)

(n.) an evil or wicked person or character, especially in a story or play
I am going to play the _____villain_____ in the show.

SYNONYMS: a scoundrel, rascal, outlaw, criminal
ANTONYMS: a hero, heroine, champion

19

Match the Meaning

For each item below, choose the word whose meaning is suggested by the clue given. Then write the word in the space provided.

1. A violent or sudden attack is called a(n) _____assault_____ .
   a. convert   b. assault   c. strategy   d. villain

2. When I carefully make a plan, I am preparing my _____strategy_____ .
   a. convert   b. dispute   c. villain   d. strategy

3. People who change their religion are _____converts_____ to the new religion.
   a. disputes   b. converts   c. strategies   d. villains

4. To give reasons for what you do is to _____justify_____ your actions.
   a. justify   b. abandon   c. assault   d. convert

5. Some advertisements can be _____misleading_____ if they leave out key details or make false claims.
   a. misleading   b. numerous   c. productive   d. impressive

6. The most wicked character in the story is the _____villain_____ .
   a. assault   b. dispute   c. villain   d. strategy

7. A vegetarian cookbook might give _____numerous_____ recipes for rice dishes and fruit salads.
   a. productive   b. shrewd   c. misleading   d. numerous

8. To give up on something is to _____abandon_____ it.
   a. assault   b. abandon   c. convert   d. justify

9. Another word for an argument or quarrel is a _____dispute_____ .
   a. convert   b. strategy   c. villain   d. dispute

10. A(n) _____productive_____ person is one who gets a lot done.
    a. productive   b. shrewd   c. misleading   d. impressive

11. The Grand Canyon is a(n) _____impressive_____ sight.
    a. shrewd   b. misleading   c. impressive   d. numerous

12. To be clever and practical is to be _____shrewd_____ .
    a. misleading   b. shrewd   c. productive   d. numerous

Synonyms

*For each item below, choose the word that is most nearly the **same** in meaning as the word or phrase in **boldface**. Then write your choice on the line provided.*

1. **change** starch to sugar
   a. abandon   b. assault   c. dispute   d. convert   _____convert_____

2. **supported** the decision
   a. abandoned b. assaulted   c. justified   d. converted   _____justified_____

3. a **thrilling** performance
   a. misleading b. numerous   c. shrewd   d. impressive   _____impressive_____

4. tried to be more **effective**
   a. numerous   b. misleading   c. productive d. shrewd   _____productive_____

5. a problem-solving **approach**
   a. strategy   b. assault   c. dispute   d. villain   _____strategy_____

6. a **crafty** move
   a. misleading b. impressive   c. shrewd   d. productive   _____shrewd_____

Antonyms

*For each item below, choose the word that is most nearly **opposite** in meaning to the word or phrase in **boldface**. Then write your choice on the line provided.*

1. **agreed with** the umpire's call
   a. disputed   b. assaulted   c. converted d. justified   _____disputed_____

2. **few** paint colors
   a. shrewd   b. misleading c. numerous d. productive   _____numerous_____

3. **occupy** the old shack
   a. assault   b. convert   c. abandon   d. justify   _____abandon_____

4. **defended** the bridge
   a. converted b. assaulted   c. disputed   d. justified   _____assaulted_____

5. the **hero** of the movie
   a. convert   b. assault   c. strategy   d. villain   _____villain_____

6. gave **accurate** directions to the tourist
   a. impressive b. misleading c. numerous d. productive   _____misleading_____

Completing the Sentence

From the list of words on pages 18–19, choose the one that best completes each item below. Then write the word in the space provided. (You may have to change the word's ending.)

GREEKS AND TROJANS AT WAR

■ Both the Greek poet Homer and the Roman poet Virgil wrote of the ten-year siege of Troy by the Greeks and of the heroes and _____ villains _____ who did battle there.

■ One of the most famous stories describes the sly _____ strategy _____ that the Greeks thought up to defeat the Trojans.

■ The Greeks had tried not once but on _____ numerous _____ occasions to force the Trojans to surrender the fortress city.

■ Several times the Greeks had _____ assaulted _____ the walls of Troy, but all of the attacks had failed.

■ Finally, the Greeks came up with a _____ shrewd _____ plan: They left at the gates of Troy a huge wooden horse as a pretended peace offering. The Trojans brought the horse inside the city walls.

■ But the wooden horse was a _____ misleading _____ gift, for hidden inside its huge body was a small army of Greeks, who at nightfall climbed from the horse and opened the gates to the city.

A FALSE SCIENCE

■ Alchemists were people who believed that it was possible to _____ convert _____ ordinary metals, such as iron and lead, into gold. The best-known alchemists are those who practiced in Europe during the Middle Ages.

■ They staged very _____ impressive _____ experiments to try to convince others that they could do as they promised.

■ Some people believed that the possibility of great wealth _____ justified _____ even the most far-fetched experiments.

■ Scientists today would _____ dispute _____ the ideas of the alchemists, but centuries ago many people believed that their ideas were sound. In fact, it was not until the 1800s that scientists proved that base metals cannot be turned into gold.

■ Failure upon failure finally persuaded most alchemists to _____ abandon _____ their dreams of wealth and glory.

■ In a way, the work that the alchemists did was _____ productive _____ because it sometimes led to advances in chemistry. During the Middle Ages, for example, alchemists were responsible for the discovery of mineral acids.

Word Associations

*Circle the letter next to the word or expression that best completes the sentence or answers the question. Pay special attention to the word in **boldface**.*

1. A person who has been **abandoned**
   a. would feel powerful
   b. would feel bold
   c. would feel happy
   d. would feel lonely

2. If you **convert** a room, you
   a. leave it the same
   b. hide in it
   c. change it
   d. take a picture of it

3. You might expect a **villain** to
   a. volunteer in a soup kitchen
   b. receive an award
   c. play the cello
   d. kidnap someone

4. A really **impressive** baseball team would
   a. use extra players
   b. lack the proper equipment
   c. lead the league
   d. play only night games

5. Which might stop an **assault**?
   a. a good night's sleep
   b. a police officer
   c. a salt shaker
   d. a rocking horse

6. A winning **strategy** involves
   a. careful planning
   b. lots of money
   c. powerful friends
   d. reckless bravery

7. On a **productive** day you would
   a. play outside
   b. get a lot done
   c. stay inside
   d. get nothing done

8. If your friends are **numerous**
   a. you have very few of them
   b. they live nearby
   c. you have a lot of them
   d. they live far away

9. **Misleading** information should usually be
   a. ignored
   b. memorized
   c. published
   d. relied upon

10. When I **justify** my claims
    a. I take them back
    b. I lose them
    c. I defend them
    d. I get sued

11. A **shrewd** person would probably
    a. get lost
    b. get a good deal
    c. get a warm welcome
    d. get fooled

12. The best way to end a **dispute** is to
    a. shake hands
    b. skip lunch
    c. argue
    d. wrestle

Unit 2 ■ *23*

Definitions

Study the spelling, pronunciation, part of speech, and definition given for each of the words below. Write the word in the blank space in the sentence that follows. Then read the synonyms and antonyms.

1. **bluff**
   (bluf)

   (adj.) direct and outspoken in a good-natured way
   He seemed a hearty, _____bluff_____ fellow.

   (n.) a steep, high cliff or bank; an attempt to fool someone
   A scout stood on a _____bluff_____ overlooking the valley.

   (v.) to deceive or trick; to try to fool others by putting on a confident front
   The thieves tried to _____bluff_____ their way past the security guard.

   SYNONYMS: (adj.) hearty; (n.) a ridge; a trick, hoax; (v.) to mislead, pretend, fake
   ANTONYMS: (adj.) insincere, artful, sly

2. **cautious**
   (kô′ shəs)

   (adj.) avoiding unnecessary risks or mistakes
   A _____cautious_____ traveler prepares for emergencies.

   SYNONYMS: careful, watchful, wary, guarded
   ANTONYMS: daring, reckless, wild

3. **consist**
   (kən sist′)

   (v.) (used with *of*) to be made up of
   Many salad dressings _____consist_____ of oil, vinegar, and spices.

   SYNONYMS: to contain, include, involve, comprise

4. **despise**
   (di spīz′)

   (v.) to look down on intensely or feel contempt for, dislike strongly
   I _____despise_____ bullies.

   SYNONYMS: to hate, scorn, detest, loathe
   ANTONYMS: to love, admire, esteem, adore, praise

5. **haven**
   (hā′ vən)

   (n.) a safe place
   The captain sought a _____haven_____ from the storm.

   SYNONYMS: a harbor, port, refuge, retreat, shelter, sanctuary
   ANTONYMS: a trap, snare, ambush

6. **miniature**
   (mi′ nē ə chur)

   (n.) a very small copy, model, or painting
   Her collection of _____miniatures_____ is quite valuable.

   (adj.) on a very small scale
   A _____miniature_____railroad was on display in the toy department of the store.

   SYNONYMS: (adj.) little, tiny, minute
   ANTONYMS: (adj.) huge, giant

Queen Victoria was Great Britain's **monarch** (word 7) from 1837 until 1901, when she died at the age of 81.

7. **monarch**
(mä' nərk)

(n.) a person who rules over a kingdom or empire
The archbishop crowned the new _____monarch_____.

SYNONYMS: a ruler, king, queen, emperor, empress, czar, sovereign
ANTONYMS: a subject, follower, commoner

8. **obstacle**
(äb' sti kəl)

(n.) something that gets in the way
Shyness need not be an _____obstacle_____ to success.

SYNONYMS: a hurdle, barrier, snag, hindrance
ANTONYMS: an aid, help, support, advantage

9. **postpone**
(pōst pōn')

(v.) to put off until later
Coach decided to _____postpone_____ the practice.

SYNONYMS: to delay, suspend, shelve, defer
ANTONYMS: to advance, move up

10. **straggle**
(stra' gəl)

(v.) to stray off or trail behind; to spread out in a scattered fashion
Latecomers continued to _____straggle_____ into the theater.

SYNONYMS: to ramble, drift, wander, roam, rove, detour

11. **treacherous**
(tre' chə rəs)

(adj.) likely to betray; seemingly safe but actually dangerous
That hill can be a _____treacherous_____ climb in winter.

SYNONYMS: disloyal, untrustworthy, unreliable; chancy, deceptive, tricky, hazardous
ANTONYMS: faithful, trustworthy; safe, harmless

12. **vivid**
(vi' vəd)

(adj.) bright and sharp, giving a clear picture; full of life
She gave a _____vivid_____ description of the daring rescue.

SYNONYMS: lively, intense, brilliant, dazzling, spirited, clear
ANTONYMS: lifeless, dull, drab, hazy, foggy

Match the Meaning

For each item below, choose the word whose meaning is suggested by the clue given. Then write the word in the space provided.

1. A picture so brilliant and bold that it seems alive might be called _____vivid_____.
   a. bluff   b. cautious   c. treacherous   d. vivid

2. A sundae _____consists_____ of ice cream and your choice of toppings.
   a. despises   b. consists   c. postpones   d. straggles

3. Something that blocks our way might be called a(n) _____obstacle_____.
   a. obstacle   b. bluff   c. haven   d. miniature

4. Hikers who stray from a trail or fall behind are guilty of _____straggling_____.
   a. consisting   b. despising   c. straggling   d. postponing

5. To try to fool others by acting very confident is to _____bluff_____.
   a. consist   b. despise   c. straggle   d. bluff

6. If you _____postpone_____ doing a chore, you will just have to do it later.
   a. bluff   b. postpone   c. straggle   d. despise

7. Walking on a decaying log that bridges a stream could be _____treacherous_____.
   a. treacherous   b. cautious   c. miniature   d. bluff

8. To hate or to dislike something strongly is to _____despise_____ it.
   a. postpone   b. bluff   c. despise   d. consist

9. Another name for king is _____monarch_____.
   a. haven   b. bluff   c. monarch   d. miniature

10. Boats seek a safe _____haven_____ where they can drop anchor for the night.
    a. bluff   b. obstacle   c. monarch   d. haven

11. A tiny copy of a full-sized object is known as a _____miniature_____.
    a. bluff   b. miniature   c. haven   d. monarch

12. To avoid unnecessary risk is to act in a _____cautious_____ way.
    a. cautious   b. vivid   c. miniature   d. treacherous

For each item below, choose the word that is most nearly the same in meaning as the word or phrase in **boldface.** Then write your choice on the line provided.

1. **fake** your way past the guard
   a. consist   b. despise   c. postpone   d. bluff   _____bluff_____

2. **wander** from the route
   a. bluff   b. straggle   c. postpone   d. despise   _____straggle_____

3. a peaceful **refuge** in the war-torn city
   a. haven   b. miniature   c. monarch   d. bluff   _____haven_____

4. a mix that **contained** flour, sugar, and baking powder
   a. bluffed   b. consisted of   c. despised   d. postponed   _____consisted of_____

5. a **watchful** driver
   a. miniature   b. treacherous   c. cautious   d. vivid   _____cautious_____

6. a noble, wise, and generous **ruler**
   a. monarch   b. haven   c. obstacle   d. miniature   _____monarch_____

Antonyms

For each item below, choose the word that is most nearly opposite in meaning to the word or phrase in **boldface.** Then write your choice on the line provided.

1. **adore** that kind of music
   a. consist   b. bluff   c. despise   d. straggle   _____despise_____

2. formed a **hazy** image
   a. treacherous   b. vivid   c. cautious   d. miniature   _____vivid_____

3. to **move up** the ceremony one month
   a. postpone   b. bluff   c. despise   d. straggle   _____postpone_____

4. a **huge** model of the castle
   a. cautious   b. treacherous   c. bluff   d. miniature   _____miniature_____

5. a **faithful** servant
   a. treacherous   b. cautious   c. miniature   d. vivid   _____treacherous_____

6. no **advantage** to winning the election
   a. haven   b. obstacle   c. miniature   d. monarch   _____obstacle_____

Completing the Sentence

From the list of words on pages 24–25, choose the one that best completes each item below. Then write the word in the space provided. (You may have to change the word's ending.)

AMERICANS FIGHT FOR THEIR INDEPENDENCE

■ King George III was the English _____ monarch _____ when American colonists began to grow impatient with English rule.

■ Even colonists who were eager for independence were _____ cautious _____ at first because they did not want a war.

■ But not all colonists _____ despised _____ British rule; nearly one-third of them believed they should stay loyal to the King.

■ The first fight took place between 700 British soldiers and a small army that _____ consisted _____ of 70 American volunteers called Minutemen. The site of the battle was Lexington, Massachusetts.

■ In 1780, the American General Benedict Arnold took part in a _____ treacherous _____ plot that nearly cost the lives of three thousand American soldiers.

■ After overcoming many _____ obstacles _____, the Americans defeated the British, and King George recognized the United States as an independent nation.

A VIEW FROM HIGH ABOVE

■ As we looked down from the rocky _____ bluff _____, we could see a small herd of wild ponies trotting in a field far below us.

■ We were so high above them that they looked like _____ miniature _____ horses.

■ One gray mare _____ straggled _____ behind the rest of the herd to protect her young foal.

A GETAWAY FOR PRESIDENTS

■ Since 1942, American presidents have used a quiet cabin retreat in Maryland as a _____ haven _____ from the summer heat of Washington, D.C.

■ My Uncle David has _____ vivid _____ memories of the occasion when President Eisenhower renamed the retreat Camp David to honor the President's grandson.

■ A crisis might cause the President to _____ postpone _____ a planned visit to Camp David until the situation is under control.

Word Associations

*Circle the letter next to the word or expression that best completes the sentence or answers the question. Pay special attention to the word in **boldface.***

1. A **vivid** performance by an actor
   a. would bore you
   b. would anger you
   c. would entertain you
   d. would disappoint you

2. A **treacherous** classmate might
   a. reveal your secrets
   b. be good at science
   c. eat too much at lunch
   d. forget to wear a bike helmet

3. A person who overcomes **obstacles**
   a. is a fast runner
   b. enjoys swimming
   c. rarely follows through
   d. does not give up easily

4. If you **straggle** on a field trip
   a. you go home early
   b. you lead the way
   c. you learn a lot
   d. you might get lost

5. A cool **haven** on a hot afternoon might be
   a. a steam bath
   b. a desert
   c. a shady tree
   d. a wool sweater

6. Some people **bluff** when they
   a. take a stroll along a cliff
   b. have lunch
   c. watch television
   d. play a game

7. If you **despise** something
   a. you are surprised by it
   b. you absolutely hate it
   c. you don't care about it
   d. you like it very much

8. A **miniature** dog would probably
   a. be a good hunter
   b. eat you out of house and home
   c. have a nasty temper
   d. be small enough to hold

9. Of what does a pizza **consist**?
   a. crust, sauce, and cheese
   b. a good appetite
   c. Italian restaurants
   d. about a dollar a slice

10. Which might be **postponed** because of rain?
    a. swim meet
    b. gymnastics meet
    c. a baseball game
    d. a basketball game

11. A **cautious** skier would probably
    a. ski only at night
    b. stay on the beginner's slopes
    c. buy used equipment
    d. perform dangerous stunts

12. Which would a **monarch** wear?
    a. a parka
    b. a baseball hat
    c. a crown
    d. a bathing suit

Definitions

Study the spelling, pronunciation, part of speech, and definition given for each of the words below. Write the word in the blank space in the sentence that follows. Then read the synonyms and antonyms.

1. **aggressive**
   (ə grē′ siv)

   (adj.) quick to fight or quarrel, tending to violence; bold and forceful, determined

   An _____aggressive_____ salesperson never gives up.

   SYNONYMS: violent, warlike; pushy, vigorous
   ANTONYMS: peaceful, timid; shy, bashful, retiring

2. **associate**
   (v., ə sō′ shē āt; n., adj., ə sō′ shē ət)

   (v.) to join or be together as partners, allies, or friends; to link in one's mind, connect

   I will always _____associate_____ peaches with summer.

   (n.) a partner, friend

   The businessman introduced his _____associate_____.

   (adj.) having less than full rank

   She was hired as an _____associate_____ professor in the English department.

   SYNONYMS: (v.) to unite, mingle, combine, mix, relate; (n.) a companion, teammate, coworker; (adj.) assistant
   ANTONYMS: (v.) to separate, distance, divorce; (n.) an enemy, foe, rival, stranger

3. **deceive**
   (di sēv′)

   (v.) to trick or lead a person into believing something that is not true

   It is unfair to _____deceive_____ the customer with false advertising.

   SYNONYMS: to fool, swindle, mislead, double-cross, cheat

4. **emigrate**
   (e′ mə grāt)

   (v.) to leave one's home country or area to live in another

   Henri hopes to _____emigrate_____ from Haiti to the United States.

   SYNONYMS: to relocate, resettle, move, migrate

5. **flexible**
   (flek′ sə bəl)

   (adj.) able to bend without breaking; able to change or to take in new ideas

   I brought in a box of _____flexible_____ straws.

   SYNONYMS: bendable, limber, elastic, springy; adaptable, adjustable
   ANTONYMS: stiff, rigid, unbendable; inflexible

6. **glamour**
   (gla′ mər)

   (n.) mysterious charm, beauty, or attractiveness

   The movie captures the _____glamour_____ of Paris.

   SYNONYMS: style, sparkle, magic, enchantment, romance, fascination

The main **span** (word 12) of the Golden Gate Bridge is 4,200 feet in length. When it was completed in 1937, it was the longest suspension bridge in the world.

7. **hazy**
(hā′ zē)

(adj.) unclear, misty; not readily seen or understandable
Another hot and _____hazy_____ *day is forecast.*
SYNONYMS: cloudy, smoggy, foggy, blurry, dim; vague
ANTONYMS: bright, clear; precise

8. **linger**
(liŋ′ gər)

(v.) to stay longer than expected, be slow in leaving; to go slowly or take one's time
We like to _____linger_____ *over breakfast on Saturdays.*
SYNONYMS: to delay, stall, remain, stay, lag, persist; to dawdle
ANTONYMS: to hurry, rush, charge, hasten

9. **luxurious**
(ləg zhúr′ ē əs)

(adj.) providing ease and comfort far beyond what is ordinary or necessary
They took a _____luxurious_____ *vacation.*
SYNONYMS: rich, elegant, pleasurable, lavish, extravagant, fancy
ANTONYMS: poor, plain, simple, modest

10. **mishap**
(mis′ hap)

(n.) an unfortunate but minor accident
The waiters chuckled over the _____mishap_____ .
SYNONYMS: a misfortune, mistake, blunder, slipup

11. **overwhelm**
(ō vər welm′)

(v.) to overcome by superior force, crush; to affect so deeply as to make helpless
Fresh troops threatened to _____overwhelm_____ *the weakened defenders.*
SYNONYMS: to overpower, destroy, crush; to stun, shock, stagger, astound

12. **span**
(span)

(n.) the full reach or length, especially between two points in space or time
The _____span_____ *of most insects' lives is very brief.*
(v.) to stretch or reach across
A new bridge will be built to _____span_____ *the river.*
SYNONYMS: (n.) extent, distance, length, scope, period; (v.) to bridge, cross, last

31

Match the Meaning

For each item below, choose the word whose meaning is suggested by the clue given. Then write the word in the space provided.

1. People who are too _____ aggressive _____ often get into quarrels or fights.
   a. flexible   b. hazy   c. luxurious   d. aggressive

2. To fool people into believing what is not true is to _____ deceive _____ them.
   a. overwhelm   b. deceive   c. emigrate   d. linger

3. If you join with me as a partner, you _____ associate _____ with me.
   a. associate   b. deceive   c. overwhelm   d. span

4. It is not easy to see distant mountains on a(n) _____ hazy _____ day.
   a. aggressive   b. flexible   c. hazy   d. luxurious

5. A princess's charm and beauty might make her a symbol of _____ glamour _____.
   a. associate   b. mishap   c. span   d. glamour

6. To _____ emigrate _____ from Korea to Nepal is to leave Korea to live in Nepal.
   a. associate   b. emigrate   c. linger   d. overwhelm

7. Getting a paper cut is an example of a minor _____ mishap _____.
   a. mishap   b. span   c. associate   d. glamour

8. A mighty army might easily _____ overwhelm _____ a weaker foe.
   a. emigrate   b. linger   c. overwhelm   d. associate

9. A(n) _____ flexible _____ straw makes it easy to drink from a juice box.
   a. luxurious   b. aggressive   c. flexible   d. hazy

10. A _____ luxurious _____ hotel might provide six fluffy bath towels for each guest.
    a. aggressive   b. hazy   c. flexible   d. luxurious

11. To stay longer than expected or to leave slowly is to _____ linger _____.
    a. deceive   b. linger   c. emigrate   d. span

12. A bridge that crosses the Mississippi is said to _____ span _____ that river.
    a. span   b. associate   c. linger   d. overwhelm

Synonyms

*For each item below, choose the word that is most nearly the **same** in meaning as the word or phrase in **boldface**. Then write your choice on the line provided.*

1. the **magic** of Hollywood
   a. mishap   b. span   c. glamour   d. associate   _____glamour_____

2. **crush** our opponents
   a. deceive   b. emigrate   c. linger   d. overwhelm   _____overwhelm_____

3. told us about the **slipup**
   a. glamour   b. span   c. mishap   d. associate   _____mishap_____

4. **move** from Egypt to Italy
   a. overwhelm   b. linger   c. deceive   d. emigrate   _____emigrate_____

5. **mislead** the enemy
   a. associate   b. deceive   c. overwhelm   d. emigrate   _____deceive_____

6. over the **period** of a year
   a. associate   b. mishap   c. span   d. glamour   _____span_____

Antonyms

*For each item below, choose the word that is most nearly **opposite** in meaning to the word or phrase in **boldface**. Then write your choice on the line provided.*

1. **timid** base runners
   a. associate   b. aggressive   c. luxurious   d. hazy   _____aggressive_____

2. introduced her **rival**
   a. glamour   b. associate   c. span   d. mishap   _____associate_____

3. **hurry** over our good-byes
   a. span   b. emigrate   c. overwhelm   d. linger   _____linger_____

4. a **rigid** point of view
   a. flexible   b. aggressive   c. hazy   d. luxurious   _____flexible_____

5. a **simple** meal with friends
   a. aggressive   b. flexible   c. luxurious   d. hazy   _____luxurious_____

6. a **clear** sky
   a. flexible   b. luxurious   c. aggressive   d. hazy   _____hazy_____

Completing the Sentence

From the list of words on pages 30–31, choose the one that best completes each item below. Then write the word in the space provided. (You may have to change the word's ending.)

A NEW LIFE IN AMERICA

■ Poor conditions in their homeland have driven many Mexicans to _____ emigrate _____ to the United States. Many have settled in the Southwest, but others have traveled to big cities in the Midwest and Northeast in search of work.

■ Some dishonest agents _____ deceive _____ travelers by taking their money in exchange for legal documents that they never provide.

■ Over the _____ span _____ of the past fifty years, more immigrants have come to the United States from Mexico than from any other country.

■ Many immigrants have only a(n) _____ hazy _____ notion of what life will be like in the new country they have heard so much about.

■ Mix-ups over language or local customs often lead to _____ mishaps _____ and misunderstandings.

■ Despite facing some _____ overwhelming _____ problems, most immigrants manage to build better lives for themselves and their families.

A LEGAL BRIEF

■ It is a lawyer's duty to act in a(n) _____ aggressive _____ fashion in order to protect the interests of his or her clients. Trial lawyers especially cannot afford to be timid or shy.

■ Most lawyers, like other professionals, have to keep _____ flexible _____ hours in order to serve their clients well.

■ From the newest _____ associate _____ to senior partners, lawyers must research past cases to find ways to support their arguments. For this reason they often spend long hours in law libraries.

■ Media attention lends some legal cases more _____ glamour _____ than they really deserve. Some especially newsworthy trials are now televised from start to finish.

■ The impact of such cases may _____ linger _____ in the public mind long after all the lawyers, the judge, and the jurors have left the courtroom.

■ Lawyers on television and in movies are often seen to drive _____ luxurious _____ cars and wear expensive clothes. In fact, most real-life lawyers work long, hard hours and rarely enjoy the spotlight of celebrity.

Word Associations

*Circle the letter next to the word or expression that best completes the sentence or answers the question. Pay special attention to the word in **boldface**.*

1. Which is an example of a **mishap**?
   a. solving a riddle
   b. a serious car accident
   c. stepping in a puddle
   d. telling a lie

2. If a movie **overwhelms** you, you
   a. might feel like you will cry
   b. might ask for a refund
   c. might refuse to clap
   d. might get very hungry

3. If you have a **hazy** grasp of map reading, you should
   a. use a brighter lamp
   b. memorize the state capitals
   c. take the bus
   d. learn more about keys and symbols

4. You might **linger** if you are
   a. not wearing a watch
   b. late for an appointment
   c. having a great time
   d. bored to tears

5. A **luxurious** outfit might include
   a. gold jewelry
   b. rags
   c. T-shirts
   d. aluminum foil

6. Which would most people **associate**?
   a. bicycles with snowshoes
   b. winter with fireworks
   c. fishing with homework
   d. vacations with summer

7. In a place known for **glamour,** a visitor might find
   a. cows grazing in a field
   b. unpaved roads
   c. lots of factories
   d. expensive restaurants

8. **Aggressive** ballplayers would
   a. lose interest in the game
   b. play as hard as they can
   c. let their opponents win
   d. ask to sit out the game

9. You might **deceive** a puppy by
   a. pretending to throw a ball
   b. taking off its collar
   c. feeding it twice a day
   d. changing your clothes

10. A U.S. citizen might **emigrate** to
    a. the moon
    b. Florida
    c. Canada
    d. New York City

11. The "**span** of a lifetime" means
    a. from Monday to Friday
    b. from birth to death
    c. from kindergarten to college
    d. from breakfast to dinner

12. Which is the most **flexible**?
    a. a frying pan
    b. a pipe wrench
    c. an extension ladder
    d. a garden hose

Unit 4 ■ 35

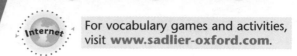

Internet

For vocabulary games and activities, visit **www.sadlier-oxford.com**.

Selecting Word Meanings

*For each of the following items, circle the choice that is most nearly the **same** in meaning as the word in **boldface**.*

1. a **myth** about the beginning of Rome
   a. fact   (b.) legend   c. trial   d. doubt

2. a **flexible** kind of plastic
   a. rigid   b. fireproof   (c.) elastic   d. slippery

3. **deceived** his partner
   a. honored   b. amused   c. soothed   (d.) double-crossed

4. a witness to the **assault**
   (a.) attack   b. accident   c. joke   d. agreement

5. **overwhelm** the enemy
   a. entertain   (b.) crush   c. outrun   d. trick

6. **reject** the application
   a. study   b. accept   c. forget   (d.) decline

7. climbed the **bluff**
   a. stairs   b. tower   (c.) bank   d. ladder

8. a **haven** for travelers
   a. map   b. show   (c.) refuge   d. tour

9. **linger** near home
   (a.) remain   b. play   c. hide   d. dig

10. **despise** cruelty to animals
    a. admire   b. outlaw   (c.) detest   d. fear

11. **abandon** the house
    a. build   b. occupy   (c.) desert   d. watch

12. a **vivid** picture
    a. small and blurry   b. dark and gloomy   (c.) bright and colorful   d. famous and expensive

Spelling

*For each item below, study the **boldface** word in which there is a blank. If a letter is missing, fill in the blank to make a correctly spelled word. If the word is already spelled correctly, leave the blank empty.*

1. **em _i_ grate** from India

2. a **min _i_ ature** poodle

3. **stra _g_ gle** into class

4. a sudden **mis _h_ ap**

5. a government **do _c_ ument**

6. a confusing **strate __ gy**

7. **con _s_ ist** of bread and water

8. a **solit _a_ ry** ladybug

9. an **impres _s_ ive** score

10. **span __** the stream

11. a **tempor _a_ ry** arrangement

12. the sneaky **vi _l_ lain**

Antonyms

*For each of the following items, circle the choice that is most nearly the **opposite** in meaning to the word in **boldface**.*

1. a **continuous** line
   a. short   b. thin   (c.) broken   d. thick

2. **justify** my decision to move
   a. defend   b. explain   (c.) question   d. regret

3. **veteran** tournament players
   (a.) inexperienced   b. skilled   c. popular   d. seasoned

4. **numerous** students
   a. many   b. happy   c. angry   (d.) few

5. a **productive** day
   a. cool   b. fruitful   (c.) inactive   d. memorable

6. turned out to be an **obstacle**
   (a.) advantage   b. enemy   c. problem   d. echo

7. **postpone** a decision
   a. delay   (b.) hasten   c. question   d. change

8. a **hazy** memory of the accident
   a. sad   b. dim   c. disturbing   (d.) clear

Vocabulary for Comprehension

*Read the following passage in which some of the words you have studied appear in **boldface**. Then answer the questions on page 39.*

The Tallest Sailor in the World

A thunderous wave crashed on Cape Cod. A loud cry split the air, and the worried villagers rushed to the beach. What they saw **overwhelmed** them. The noise had come from a **solitary** baby—a baby who was 6 feet tall! The locals put the giant baby in a cart and hauled him into town. They named him Alfred Bulltop Stormalong but called him Stormy.

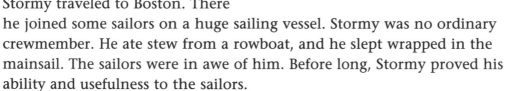

Stormy grew to love the sea. He loved swimming in the deep water and riding the sea monsters. He was fearless. Once he even turned an abandoned house upside down and tried to sail away in it.

Stormy grew to be 36 feet tall, and Cape Cod became too small. **Abandoning** Cape Code, Stormy traveled to Boston. There he joined some sailors on a huge sailing vessel. Stormy was no ordinary crewmember. He ate stew from a rowboat, and he slept wrapped in the mainsail. The sailors were in awe of him. Before long, Stormy proved his ability and usefulness to the sailors.

Stormalong's sailing skills were **impressive**, too. In one adventure, Stormy was sailing *The Courser* through the English Channel when he discovered that the waterway was only 6 inches wider than *The Courser*. Expecting a tight fit, Stormy told the crew to soap the sides of the ship. *The Courser* slipped through, but not without **mishap**. The huge ship scraped the Dover Cliffs, leaving behind a thick layer of soap. These cliffs have been pure white ever since. Folks there say that the Channel is still foamy from the soap.

*Fill in the circle next to the choice that best completes the sentence
or answers the question.*

1. This passage is mostly about
   - (a) the work sailors do
   - (b) how to become a sailor
   - (c) life in old New England
   - (d) one unusual sailor

2. The meaning of **overwhelmed** is
   - (a) astounded
   - (b) exhausted
   - (c) amused
   - (d) useless

3. In this passage, **solitary** means
   - (a) friendly
   - (b) temporary
   - (c) just one
   - (d) tiny

4. Alfred Bulltop Stormalong spent most of his time
   - (a) in Boston
   - (b) near or at sea
   - (c) far inland
   - (d) on *The Courser*

5. Stormy was different from the other sailors because
   - (a) he was less experienced than they were
   - (b) he was a hated villain
   - (c) he was sensitive and fragile
   - (d) he was very tall

6. In this passage, the meaning of **abandoning** is
   - (a) visiting
   - (b) forsaking
   - (c) occupying
   - (d) crossing

7. **Impressive** most nearly means
   - (a) commanding attention
   - (b) fading away
   - (c) plentiful
   - (d) continuous

8. What was *The Courser*?
   - (a) a submarine
   - (b) a battleship
   - (c) a sailing ship
   - (d) a fishing boat

9. Another word for **mishap** is
   - (a) reminder
   - (b) scuffle
   - (c) accident
   - (d) spin

10. According to the passage, what made the Dover Cliffs white?
    - (a) chalk
    - (b) sand
    - (c) sea foam
    - (d) soap

Grammar in Context

A **run-on sentence** is two or more sentences that run together. When you read a run-on sentence, it is hard to tell where one idea ends and a new one begins.

He ate stew from a rowboat he slept wrapped in the mainsail. ← **run-on sentence**

To fix a run-on sentence:

- Rewrite the sentence as two separate sentences.

   He ate stew from a rowboat. He slept wrapped in the mainsail.

   OR

- Rewrite the sentence as a compound sentence. Add a comma and the conjunction *and*, *but*, or *or* to join the sentences.

   He ate stew from a rowboat, **and** he slept wrapped in the mainsail.

Fix each run-on sentence. Write it as two separate sentences, or rewrite it as a compound sentence.   Possible answers are given.

1. It was a hot and hazy day Stormy was ready to set sail. It was a hot and hazy day, and Stormy was ready to set sail.

2. Stormy knew that the seas could be treacherous he was not afraid. Stormy knew that the seas could be treacherous, but he was not afraid.

3. The sailors pulled hard on the anchor numerous times it did not budge. The sailors pulled hard on the anchor numerous times, but it did not budge.

4. The veteran crew could keep tugging they could let Stormy try. The veteran crew could keep tugging, or they could let Stormy try.

5. The sailors abandoned the smaller ship they built a bigger one. The sailors abandoned the smaller ship. They built a bigger one.

6. Stormy went west his stay was temporary. Stormy went west, but his stay was temporary.

 **Completing the Idea**

*Complete each sentence so that it makes sense. Pay attention to the word in **boldface**.*

Accept answers that show an understanding of the vocabulary.

1. We had to **cancel** the picnic when _____.

2. I **associate** the month of June with _____.

3. At last, we ended the **dispute** by _____.

4. I can **justify** my actions by _____.

5. The directions were so **misleading** that I _____.

6. We had to **postpone** the game because _____.

7. I am **cautious** when I _____.

8. My favorite dessert **consists** of _____.

9. The cool shade is my **haven** when _____.

10. If I **straggle** at the airport, I might _____.

11. Dancers stay **flexible** so they can _____.

12. The photo was so **vivid** I could _____.

13. Because our dog can be **aggressive**, we _____.

14. When I imagine **glamour**, I picture _____.

15. I might **linger** in the hallway after school because _____.

Write Your Own

Choose a word from Units 1–4. Write a sentence using the word. Be sure the sentence is not a run-on.

Check that the vocabulary is used correctly and that the sentence is written correctly.

_____

*The words in **boldface** in the sentences below are related to words introduced in Units 1–4. For example, the nouns* justification *and* cancellation *in item 1 are related to the verbs* justify *(Unit 2) and* cancel *(Unit 1). Based on your understanding of the unit words that follow, circle the related word in **boldface** that best completes each sentence.*

aggressive	associate	cancel	cautious	consist
convert	deceive	distribute	document	emigrate
flexible	glamour	justify	luxurious	myth
postpone	reject	straggle	strategy	treacherous

1. Blizzard conditions led to the (**justification/cancellation**) of flights throughout the upper Midwest.

2. Unicorns and dragons are classic examples of (**mythical/strategic**) animals.

3. The potato famine of the 1840s led to the (**flexibility/emigration**) of hundreds of thousands of Irish to the United States.

4. One should always use extreme (**caution/distribution**) when approaching a wild animal.

5. Our guide warned the (**associations/stragglers**) that they might get lost if they didn't keep up with the rest of the tour group.

6. The traitor Benedict Arnold is better known for his (**treachery/luxury**) than for his earlier service to the American cause.

7. A buyer of a painting by an Old Master will want to see some (**aggression/documentation**) that proves it is not a fake.

8. The melted ice cream tasted sweet but had the (**consistency/postponement**) of soup.

9. The downtown areas of some cities are coming to life once again thanks to the (**conversion/rejection**) of old factory buildings into shops and housing.

10. Some who go to Hollywood in search of fame and fortune find that life there is not so (**deceptive/glamorous**) as they have been led to believe.

Word Games

Use the clue and the given letters to complete each word. Write the missing letters of the word in the appropriate boxes. Then use the circled letters and the drawing to answer the CHALLENGE question below.

1. Not to be trusted

T R E (A) C H E R O U S

2. Tending to use force or violence

A G G R E S S I (V) E

3. Constant or unbroken

C O N T (I) N U O U S

4. A brief tussle or fist fight

S C U F F (L) E

5. A king or queen

M O (N) A R C H

6. Rich and elegant

(L) U X U R I O U S

7. Mix or join with

A S S O C (I) A T E

Challenge:

What am I?

V I L L A I N

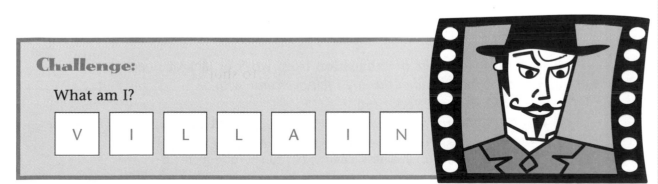

Definitions

Study the spelling, pronunciation, part of speech, and definition given for each of the words below. Write the word in the blank space in the sentence that follows. Then read the synonyms and antonyms.

1. **blemish**
   (ble' mish)

   (n.) a mark or stain that damages the appearance of something; a weakness or flaw

   The carpenter noticed a _____blemish_____ in the finish of the cabinet.

   SYNONYMS: a scar, spot, smudge; a defect, weak spot

2. **blunt**
   (blunt)

   (adj.) having a dull point or edge, not sharp; honest but insensitive in manner

   My uncle gave me some _____blunt_____ advice.

   (v.) to make less sharp

   Misuse will _____blunt_____ a knife blade.

   SYNONYMS: (adj.) dull; outspoken, frank, direct
   ANTONYMS: (adj.) sharp, keen; tactful, diplomatic; (v.) to sharpen

3. **capable**
   (kā' pə bəl)

   (adj.) able and prepared to do something; fit or skilled

   A _____capable_____ teacher should be rewarded.

   SYNONYM: qualified
   ANTONYMS: unqualified, incapable, unfit

4. **conclude**
   (kən klüd')

   (v.) to finish; to bring something to an end; to decide after careful thought

   After electing a new secretary, the committee voted to _____conclude_____ the meeting.

   SYNONYMS: to close, complete, stop; to reason, judge
   ANTONYMS: to open, begin, start, commence

5. **detect**
   (di tekt')

   (v.) to find or discover something, notice

   A test may _____detect_____ chemicals in the water supply.

   SYNONYMS: to observe, spot
   ANTONYMS: to miss, overlook

6. **fatigue**
   (fə tēg')

   (n.) weariness or exhaustion from work or lack of sleep

   By the end of the day I felt overcome with _____fatigue_____.

   (v.) to make very tired

   The riders were warned not to _____fatigue_____ the horses.

   SYNONYMS: (n.) tiredness, sleepiness, weakness; (v.) to tire
   ANTONYMS: (n.) liveliness, energy; (v.) to energize, perk up

Internet
For vocabulary games and activities,
visit **www.sadlier-oxford.com**.

A Bedouin is shown here leading camels across the desert. Bedouins are **nomads** (word 9) who speak Arabic and live in the Middle East.

7. **festive**
(fes' tiv)

(adj.) having to do with a feast or celebration
Decorations will help lend a _____ festive _____ atmosphere.

SYNONYMS: happy, merry, playful
ANTONYMS: sad, gloomy, somber

8. **hospitality**
(häs pə ta' lə tē)

(n.) a friendly welcome and treatment of guests
The innkeepers were famous for their _____ hospitality _____.

SYNONYMS: friendliness, generosity, warmth
ANTONYMS: unfriendliness, hostility

9. **nomad**
(nō' mad)

(n.) a member of a people who move from place to place; a person who roams aimlessly
The adventurer lived the life of a _____ nomad _____.

SYNONYMS: a wanderer, roamer, rover

10. **persecute**
(pûr' si kyüt)

(v.) to treat unjustly or cause to suffer
The dictator may try to _____ persecute _____ the minority group.

SYNONYMS: to torment, hurt, annoy
ANTONYMS: to reward, favor, comfort, help, protect

11. **supreme**
(sə prēm')

(adj.) highest in power, rank, authority, quality, or degree
He acted as if giving up his seat were the _____ supreme _____ sacrifice.

SYNONYMS: first, greatest, dominant, outstanding
ANTONYMS: low, lowly, worst

12. **transport**
(*v.,* trans pôrt';
n., trans' pôrt)

(v.) to move or carry from one place to another
A mover was hired to _____ transport _____ the furniture.

(n.) a vehicle used to move things from place to place; the act or process of moving something from one place to another
The ocean liner was used as troop _____ transport _____ during the war.

SYNONYMS: (v.) to haul, cart, send, convey

Match the Meaning

For each item below, choose the word whose meaning is suggested by the clue given. Then write the word in the space provided.

1. People who never settle down in one place are called _____nomads_____.
   a. blemishes   b. transports   c. hospitalities   d. nomads

2. To _____persecute_____ someone is to be cruel to that person.
   a. conclude   b. persecute   c. blunt   d. detect

3. To prove your ability at something is to show yourself _____capable_____.
   a. capable   b. festive   c. supreme   d. blunt

4. A train is a good form of _____transport_____ if you want to enjoy the scenery.
   a. nomad   b. transport   c. blemish   d. fatigue

5. Weddings and birthdays are examples of _____festive_____ events.
   a. blunt   b. capable   c. festive   d. supreme

6. To notice something is to _____detect_____ it.
   a. detect   b. conclude   c. persecute   d. blunt

7. You can usually overcome _____fatigue_____ by getting a good night's sleep.
   a. transport   b. hospitality   c. fatigue   d. blemishes

8. The _____Supreme_____ Court is the highest in the land.
   a. Supreme   b. Blunt   c. Festive   d. Capable

9. It's a good idea to _____conclude_____ a speech with a summary.
   a. blunt   b. conclude   c. detect   d. persecute

10. A smudge in a paint job is an example of a _____blemish_____.
    a. hospitality   b. transport   c. nomad   d. blemish

11. Improper use of a knife may _____blunt_____ its edge.
    a. detect   b. transport   c. blunt   d. conclude

12. Good hosts would be sure to show _____hospitality_____.
    a. transport   b. hospitality   c. blemish   d. fatigue

Synonyms

*For each item below, choose the word that is most nearly the **same** in meaning as the word or phrase in **boldface**. Then write your choice on the line provided.*

1. her **outstanding** accomplishment
   a. blunt   b. festive   c. supreme   d. capable   _____supreme_____

2. tried to conceal the **flaw**
   a. blemish   b. nomad   c. fatigue   d. hospitality   _____blemish_____

3. **carry** the grain to distant markets
   a. conclude   b. detect   c. blunt   d. transport   _____transport_____

4. a **skilled** performer, but not a star
   a. supreme   b. capable   c. blunt   d. festive   _____capable_____

5. followed the trail of **wanderers**
   a. transports   b. blemishes   c. nomads   d. hospitalities   _____nomads_____

6. a **happy** atmosphere
   a. festive   b. capable   c. supreme   d. blunt   _____festive_____

Antonyms

*For each item below, choose the word that is most nearly **opposite** in meaning to the word or phrase in **boldface**. Then write your choice on the line provided.*

1. **overlook** the danger
   a. detect   b. conclude   c. persecute   d. transport   _____detect_____

2. spoke in a **diplomatic** manner
   a. supreme   b. festive   c. blunt   d. capable   _____blunt_____

3. **begin** the homework project
   a. detect   b. persecute   c. transport   d. conclude   _____conclude_____

4. **protected** the strangers
   a. blunted   b. persecuted   c. concluded   d. detected   _____persecuted_____

5. surprised by their **liveliness**
   a. nomad   b. blemish   c. fatigue   d. hospitality   _____fatigue_____

6. showed **unfriendliness** to the visitors
   a. fatigue   b. hospitality   c. transports   d. blemishes   _____hospitality_____

Completing the Sentence

From the list of words on pages 44–45, choose the one that best completes each item below. Then write the word in the space provided. (You may have to change the word's ending.)

SPEAKING OUT AGAINST BIAS

■ The principal did not mince her words but spoke in _____blunt_____ terms on the subject of prejudice to the students assembled in the school auditorium.

■ She described the ugly insult that had been written on a wall as a _____blemish_____ on the school's honor.

■ She went on to warn that she would not allow a handful of students to be _____persecuted_____ just because they held different religious beliefs from most.

■ "Sometimes it requires a _____supreme_____ effort," she said, "to overcome our prejudices and respect the diginity of others. But it is an effort that all civilized people must make."

■ She asked that everyone work together to make ours a school that is known for the _____hospitality_____ it shows to all.

ON THE MOVE

■ Though many Native American peoples lived in settled villages and tilled the land, many others lived the life of _____nomads_____.

■ The nomadic tribes of the Great Plains marked successful buffalo hunts with _____festive_____ ceremonies of thanks.

■ In Asia the nomadic Kazakhs use camels to _____transport_____ their tents, called *yurts*, and other belongings from place to place.

■ Because they lose body water very slowly, camels are _____capable_____ of traveling for days, even in extreme heat, without drinking a drop. When they do have water to drink, they can consume as much as 25 gallons in ten minutes!

A TRAIN DERAILS

■ The safety panel looking into the train crash _____concluded_____ that the most likely cause was human error.

■ It was learned that the engineer had not slept in over 36 hours and was probably suffering from extreme _____fatigue_____.

■ Furthermore, tests of the equipment did not _____detect_____ any signs of failure in the train's braking system.

*Circle the letter next to the word or expression that best completes the sentence or answers the question. Pay special attention to the word in **boldface**.*

1. If you feel **fatigue**, you might
   a. take a nap
   b. run 3 miles
   c. swim 50 laps
   d. clean out the garage

2. Which *cannot* offer **hospitality**?
   a. a school
   b. a gift box
   c. a town
   d. a person

3. Someone who is **blunt** might
   a. cheer you up
   b. hurt your feelings
   c. lie to you
   d. forget your birthday

4. Which is a **festive** event?
   a. a final exam
   b. a terrible tragedy
   c. a birthday party
   d. a criminal trial

5. A **capable** student is one who
   a. travels a long way to school
   b. misses a lot of school
   c. does well in school
   d. knows everyone in school

6. Which of the following might you use
   to **detect** something?
   a. a pencil
   b. a magnifying glass
   c. a sandwich
   d. a pair of scissors

7. A **blemished** jewel will probably
   a. cost less than a flawless one
   b. be stolen
   c. be found in a museum
   d. cost more than a flawless one

8. A good detective might **conclude** a
   robbery case by
   a. turning in her badge
   b. looking for clues
   c. having donuts and coffee
   d. arresting the thief

9. Your **supreme** achievement is
   a. your greatest
   b. your worst
   c. your first
   d. your last

10. A **nomad's** home might be
    a. an apartment
    b. a castle
    c. a tent
    d. a farmhouse

11. If I were **persecuted,** I would
    a. feel happy
    b. feel hungry
    c. feel hurt
    d. feel sleepy

12. Which might **transport** an elephant?
    a. a skateboard
    b. a shopping cart
    c. a hot-air balloon
    d. a big truck

Definitions

Study the spelling, pronunciation, part of speech, and definition given for each of the words below. Write the word in the blank space in the sentence that follows. Then read the synonyms and antonyms.

1. **accomplish**
   (ə käm′ plish)

   (v.) to do, make happen, succeed in, carry through
   Let's work together to _____accomplish_____ *the task.*

   SYNONYMS: to perform, fulfill, achieve, complete
   ANTONYMS: to fail, undo, fall short

2. **apparent**
   (ə par′ ənt)

   (adj.) open to view; easy to understand; seeming to be true or real
   Speeding was the _____apparent_____ *cause of the accident.*

   SYNONYMS: clear, obvious, visible; plain; likely
   ANTONYMS: hidden, concealed; difficult, uncertain

3. **capacity**
   (kə pa′ sə tē)

   (n.) the amount of space that can be filled; ability or skill; office or role
   The stadium was filled to _____capacity_____ *for the championship game.*

   SYNONYMS: volume, size, room; gift; position, job

4. **civilian**
   (sə vil′ yən)

   (n.) a person not on active duty in a military, police, or firefighting force
   A team of _____civilians_____ *investigated the accident.*
   (adj.) nonmilitary
   No _____civilian_____ *casualties were reported.*

   SYNONYM: (n. & adj.) nonmilitary
   ANTONYM: (n. & adj.) military

5. **conceal**
   (kən sēl′)

   (v.) to hide or keep secret, to place out of sight
   I tried to _____conceal_____ *my disappointment with a smile.*

   SYNONYMS: to cover, disguise, mask, tuck away
   ANTONYMS: to uncover, open, reveal

6. **duplicate**
   (v., dü′ pli kāt;
   n., adj., dü′ pli kət)

   (v.) to copy exactly; to produce something equal to
   A locksmith can _____duplicate_____ *almost any key.*
   (adj.) exactly like something else
   My friend and I came up with _____duplicate_____ *plans.*
   (n.) an exact copy
   He hung up a framed _____duplicate_____ *of a famous painting in his office.*

   SYNONYMS: (v.) to reproduce, clone; (adj.) identical; (n.) a reproduction, replica
   ANTONYM: (n.) an original

It was a fad in the 1960s to test the **capacity**
(word 3) of little cars by seeing how many
people could fit inside them.

7. keen
(kēn)

(adj.) having a sharpened edge; quick and sharp in thought or in sight, hearing, or smell; eager

Birds of prey have _____ keen _____ *eyesight.*

SYNONYMS: razor-edged; acute, alert; ready
ANTONYMS: dull, blunt; lazy, unwilling

8. provoke
(prə vōk')

(v.) to annoy or make angry, stir up; to do something in order to get a response

Name-calling is bound to _____ provoke _____ *an argument.*

SYNONYMS: to excite, enrage, madden, goad
ANTONYMS: to calm, soothe, pacify, quiet

9. spurt
(spûrt)

(v.) to shoot out quickly in a stream; to show a burst of energy

We watched the runners _____ spurt _____ *for the finish line.*

(n.) a sudden, short stream of fluid; a quick burst of activity

My shirt was stained by a _____ spurt _____ *of ketchup.*

SYNONYMS: (v.) to squirt, gush, flow; (n.) a jet, surge

10. undoing
(ən dü' iŋ)

(n.) a bringing to ruin or destruction; the cause of ruin; unfastening or loosening

Idle gossip was the cause of their _____ undoing _____ *.*

SYNONYMS: downfall, misfortune, trouble; an opening
ANTONYMS: good luck, fortune, success; fastening

11. vast
(vast)

(adj.) very great or very large

A _____ vast _____ *desert stretched into the distance.*

SYNONYMS: huge, enormous, spacious
ANTONYMS: tiny, small, little, narrow

12. withdraw
(with drô')

(v.) to pull out or remove; to move back or away, retreat

Is it too late to _____ withdraw _____ *from the race?*

SYNONYMS: to subtract; to leave, depart
ANTONYMS: to deposit, enter; to attack

Match the Meaning

For each item below, choose the word whose meaning is suggested by the clue given. Then write the word in the space provided.

1. Your teacher might use a copier to _____duplicate_____ an assignment.
   a. provoke   b. duplicate   c. accomplish   d. spurt

2. A person who is not part of the military is a(n) _____civilian_____.
   a. civilian   b. capacity   c. spurt   d. undoing

3. To remove something is to _____withdraw_____ it.
   a. provoke   b. conceal   c. withdraw   d. duplicate

4. The number of people who can fit into a room depends upon its _____capacity_____.
   a. capacity   b. spurts   c. duplicates   d. civilians

5. Something that seems obvious is said to be _____apparent_____.
   a. keen   b. vast   c. apparent   d. civilian

6. A(n) _____spurt_____ from a garden hose might get you wet.
   a. undoing   b. duplicate   c. spurt   d. capacity

7. A(n) _____keen_____ blade will cut much better than a dull one.
   a. keen   b. apparent   c. vast   d. civilian

8. If you tease someone, you might _____provoke_____ that person.
   a. accomplish   b. conceal   c. provoke   d. withdraw

9. A serious mistake might lead to one's _____undoing_____.
   a. capacity   b. spurt   c. civilian   d. undoing

10. To hide something is to _____conceal_____ it.
    a. accomplish   b. conceal   c. provoke   d. withdraw

11. The Atlantic Ocean is a(n) _____vast_____ body of water.
    a. keen   b. duplicate   c. apparent   d. vast

12. When you reach your goal, you have _____accomplished_____ something.
    a. concealed   b. withdrawn   c. duplicated   d. accomplished

Synonyms

*For each item below, choose the word that is most nearly the **same** in meaning as the word or phrase in **boldface.** Then write your choice on the line provided.*

1. create an **identical** set of plans
   a. vast   b. duplicate   c. keen   d. apparent   __duplicate__

2. measured the trunk's **room**
   a. capacity   b. spurt   c. civilian   d. undoing   __capacity__

3. **complete** the mission in two weeks
   a. provoke   b. duplicate   c. accomplish d. withdraw   __accomplish__

4. led to the **downfall** of the dictator
   a. civilian   b. spurt   c. capacity   d. undoing   __undoing__

5. **depart** from the battlefield
   a. withdraw   b. provoke   c. spurt   d. conceal   __withdraw__

6. water that **squirted** from the hose
   a. concealed   b. spurted   c. withdrew   d. provoked   __spurted__

Antonyms

*For each item below, choose the word that is most nearly **opposite** in meaning to the word or phrase in **boldface.** Then write your choice on the line provided.*

1. **hidden** reasons
   a. apparent   b. keen   c. civilian   d. vast   __apparent__

2. a **military** operation
   a. apparent   b. civilian   c. keen   d. vast   __civilian__

3. a **small** field
   a. keen   b. duplicate   c. civilian   d. vast   __vast__

4. **calm** the animal
   a. provoke   b. conceal   c. duplicate   d. accomplish   __provoke__

5. **reveal** the answers
   a. duplicate   b. provoke   c. conceal   d. withdraw   __conceal__

6. a **dull** sense of humor
   a. vast   b. civilian   c. duplicate   d. keen   __keen__

Completing the Sentence

From the list of words on pages 50–51, choose the one that best completes each item below. Then write the word in the space provided. (You may have to change the word's ending.)

From the list of words on pages 50–51

REVOLUTION IN AMERICA AND FRANCE

■ One of the events that led to the American Revolution was the Boston Massacre, when British soldiers fired into a crowd of _____**civilians**_____.

■ Some historians say that the soldiers were _____**provoked**_____ into firing by the insults and taunts of the crowd.

■ It soon became _____**apparent**_____ to the British—even those who preferred not to see it—that the American colonies would settle for nothing less than full independence.

■ The leaders of the French Revolution were inspired by the American Revolution and hoped to _____**duplicate**_____ its success.

■ The Revolution in France led to the death of King Louis and the _____**undoing**_____ of the old order.

A CALIFORNIA DESERT

■ With an area of 25,000 square miles, the Mojave Desert covers a(n) _____**vast**_____ portion of southern California. On the desert's border is Death Valley, the lowest point in North America.

■ During the daytime some animals, such as the kangaroo rat, _____**withdraw**_____ from the hot desert floor to cooler underground burrows.

■ Though the desert roadrunner is a poor flier, it can run in quick _____**spurts**_____ to capture its prey. The roadrunner feeds on lizards, snakes, and insects.

THE SIXTEENTH PRESIDENT

■ In his _____**capacity**_____ as commander in chief, Abraham Lincoln played an important part in choosing the generals of the Union armies.

■ One of Lincoln's choices was Ulysses S. Grant, who _____**accomplished**_____ what no other Union general before him had been able to do—force the surrender of Robert E. Lee.

■ Lincoln's aides so feared for his safety that they often went to great lengths to _____**conceal**_____ his movements.

■ The many examples of his jokes and stories show that Lincoln possessed a(n) _____**keen**_____ sense of humor.

*Circle the letter next to the word or expression that best completes the sentence or answers the question. Pay special attention to the word in **boldface**.*

1. To **duplicate** a recipe, you might
   a. change it
   b. copy it
   c. memorize it
   d. hide it

2. When you **provoke** someone, that person is likely
   a. to thank you
   b. to forget you
   c. to be angry with you
   d. to praise you

3. Which is a **vast** distance?
   a. between Earth and Mars
   b. between your ears
   c. between footsteps
   d. between telephone poles

4. To **accomplish** something, you must
   a. think negative thoughts
   b. have lunch
   c. start at the beginning
   d. forget about it

5. You might **conceal** yourself
   a. in a chair
   b. on a busy sidewalk
   c. in a closet
   d. on top of your desk

6. Which is *not* a **civilian**?
   a. a teacher
   b. a lawyer
   c. a police officer
   d. a plumber

7. If you feel a **spurt** of energy, you
   a. might run faster
   b. might take a nap
   c. might go to the doctor
   d. might take a vitamin

8. People who have **keen** hearing
   a. can barely hear a loud siren
   b. need to have their ears examined
   c. would talk loudly
   d. can hear a pin drop

9. One of the things about you that is most **apparent** is
   a. your birthday
   b. the number of siblings you have
   c. the color of your hair
   d. whether or not you have a pet

10. You might measure the **capacity** of
    a. a bathtub
    b. a shower curtain
    c. a bar of soap
    d. a bath mat

11. Which might be a diet's **undoing**?
    a. lots of willpower
    b. lots of exercise
    c. lack of desserts
    d. lack of willpower

12. When a turtle **withdraws** its head, it
    a. wants you to pet its head
    b. pulls its head into its shell
    c. stretches its neck
    d. is ready to race

Definitions

Study the spelling, pronunciation, part of speech, and definition given for each of the words below. Write the word in the blank space in the sentence that follows. Then read the synonyms and antonyms.

1. **barrier**
(bar' ē ər)

(n.) something that blocks the way; an obstacle
Volunteers worked feverishly to build a _____ barrier _____ that would keep the forest fire from spreading.

SYNONYMS: an obstruction, fence, wall, blockade, safeguard
ANTONYMS: an opening, passage

2. **calculate**
(kal' kyə lāt)

(v.) to find out by using mathematics, reckon; to find out by reasoning, estimate
The math teacher asked us to _____ calculate _____ the number of hours we spend on homework each week.

SYNONYMS: to gauge, figure, determine, judge

3. **compose**
(kəm pōz')

(v.) to be or make up the parts of, form; to create or write; to calm or quiet one's mind
Before you _____ compose _____ the essay, you might write an outline.

SYNONYMS: to produce, invent; to still, settle
ANTONYMS: to annoy, disturb

4. **considerable**
(kən sid' ər ə bəl)

(adj.) fairly large in size or extent; worthy of attention
It will take a _____ considerable _____ amount of time to complete the science project.

SYNONYMS: great, sizable, major, important
ANTONYMS: small, slight, negligible

5. **deputy**
(de' pyə tē)

(n.) one chosen to help or take the place of another or to act in that person's absence
The sheriff's first act after winning the election was to appoint a _____ deputy _____.

SYNONYMS: an assistant, aide, substitute

6. **industrious**
(in dus' trē əs)

(adj.) busy, working steadily
The crew that gathered to clean up the vacant lot were as _____ industrious _____ as ants.

SYNONYMS: active, occupied, energetic, untiring
ANTONYMS: lazy, idle, loafing, slow

For vocabulary games and activities, visit **www.sadlier-oxford.com**.

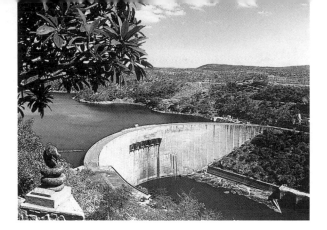

A dam is a **barrier** (word 1) constructed to control the flow of water. The dam shown here is the Kariba in the African nation of Zimbabwe.

7. **jolt**
   (jōlt)

   (v.) to shake up roughly; to move along in a jerky or bumpy fashion
   It was fun to _____jolt_____ down the dirt road in the wagon.

   (n.) a sudden bump or jerk; a shock or surprise
   We felt a _____jolt_____ as the Ferris wheel started.

   SYNONYMS: (v.) to jar, rattle, hit; (n.) a lurch, bounce

8. **loot**
   (lüt)

   (v.) to rob by force or violence, especially during war or time of unrest
   The soldiers were warned not to _____loot_____ the villages.

   (n.) valuable things that have been stolen or taken by force
   Detectives found _____loot_____ from a dozen robberies.

   SYNONYMS: (v.) to steal, plunder; (n.) prize, spoils

9. **rejoice**
   (ri jois')

   (v.) to feel joy or great delight; to make joyful
   The whole town will _____rejoice_____ if the team wins the championship.

   SYNONYMS: to celebrate, cheer
   ANTONYMS: to grieve, mourn

10. **reliable**
    (re lī' ə bəl)

    (adj.) deserving trust, dependable
    It is not easy to find a _____reliable_____ babysitter.

    SYNONYMS: faithful, proven, trustworthy
    ANTONYMS: unreliable, questionable, fickle

11. **senseless**
    (sens' ləs)

    (adj.) lacking meaning, stupid or foolish; without use of the senses
    The boxer was knocked _____senseless_____ by the blow.

    SYNONYMS: ridiculous, silly, illogical, birdbrained; unconscious
    ANTONYMS: brilliant, clever, smart

12. **shrivel**
    (shriv' əl)

    (v.) to shrink and wrinkle, especially from heat, cold, or dryness
    Exposed skin will _____shrivel_____ in the frosty air.

    SYNONYMS: to wither, dry, contract
    ANTONYMS: to expand, enlarge, swell

Match the Meaning

For each item below, choose the word whose meaning is suggested by the clue given. Then write the word in the space provided.

1. _____Industrious_____ people always stay busy by finding things to do.
   a. considerable   b. senseless   c. reliable   d. industrious

2. Because we forgot to water the plants, they all _____shriveled_____.
   a. composed   b. shriveled   c. calculated   d. rejoiced

3. When I ride my bike on an unpaved road, I feel a _____jolt_____ with each bump.
   a. jolt   b. barrier   c. deputy   d. loot

4. An action without meaning may be called _____senseless_____.
   a. industrious   b. considerable   c. senseless   d. reliable

5. Something that poses an obstacle is called a _____barrier_____.
   a. jolt   b. deputy   c. loot   d. barrier

6. Add the cost of all the food and drinks, as well as the tax and tip, to
   _____calculate_____ the total cost of the meal.
   a. jolt   b. calculate   c. rejoice   d. compose

7. A person chosen to act in another's absence is a _____deputy_____.
   a. deputy   b. loot   c. jolt   d. barrier

8. Calm yourself and quiet your mind to _____compose_____ your thoughts.
   a. calculate   b. rejoice   c. compose   d. jolt

9. A(n) _____considerable_____ number is a pretty large one.
   a. reliable   b. industrious   c. considerable   d. senseless

10. A(n) _____reliable_____ car starts up every morning, even in winter.
    a. industrious   b. senseless   c. considerable   d. reliable

11. To celebrate with delight is to _____rejoice_____.
    a. shrivel   b. rejoice   c. calculate   d. compose

12. The robbers stashed their _____loot_____ in an old refrigerator.
    a. loot   b. barrier   c. deputy   d. jolt

Synonyms

For each item below, choose the word that is most nearly the **same** in meaning as the word or phrase in **boldface.** Then write your choice on the line provided.

1. knocked **unconscious** when I fell off the ladder
   a. industrious   b. senseless   c. considerable   d. reliable   _____senseless_____

2. **jarred** by the rough landing
   a. jolted   b. composed   c. shriveled   d. looted   _____jolted_____

3. **produce** a long poem
   a. jolt   b. calculate   c. compose   d. rejoice   _____compose_____

4. call the **assistant** for help
   a. barrier   b. loot   c. deputy   d. jolt   _____deputy_____

5. **determine** the cost of painting the apartment
   a. compose   b. rejoice   c. jolt   d. calculate   _____calculate_____

6. would **plunder** the house while the owners were away
   a. jolt   b. compose   c. loot   d. calculate   _____loot_____

Antonyms

For each item below, choose the word that is most nearly **opposite** in meaning to the word or phrase in **boldface.** Then write your choice on the line provided.

1. the **idle** carpenter
   a. considerable   b. industrious   c. reliable   d. senseless   _____industrious_____

2. **swell** in the heat
   a. calculate   b. jolt   c. compose   d. shrivel   _____shrivel_____

3. **mourn** over the election results
   a. loot   b. calculate   c. rejoice   d. shrivel   _____rejoice_____

4. made a **slight** difference
   a. considerable   b. industrious   c. senseless   d. reliable   _____considerable_____

5. a **questionable** source of information
   a. industrious   b. considerable   c. reliable   d. senseless   _____reliable_____

6. found an **opening**
   a. deputy   b. loot   c. jolt   d. barrier   _____barrier_____

Completing the Sentence

From the list of words on pages 56–57, choose the one that best completes each item below. Then write the word in the space provided. (You may have to change the word's ending.)

EARTHQUAKE!

■ The powerful earthquake that hit the San Francisco Bay area on October 17, 1989, did _____considerable_____ damage to the city, though not nearly so much as was done by the terrible earthquake and fire of 1906.

■ The mighty _____jolt_____, which registered 7.1 on the Richter scale, shook buildings and buckled elevated highways.

■ Safety officials quickly put up _____barriers_____ to keep people away from unsafe areas.

■ Scientists _____calculated_____ that the loss of life and property would have been far greater if the earthquake had hit during the day instead of early evening.

A GREAT ARTIST

■ The Dutch painter Vincent van Gogh was an ambitious and _____industrious_____ artist who made hundreds of paintings and drawings during his short lifetime. He moved to southern France in 1888, and there he produced many of his masterpieces. Van Gogh died in 1890 at the age of 37.

■ Van Gogh _____rejoiced_____ at the completion of each new painting but despaired that his work never sold.

■ As the summer heat _____shriveled_____ the olives on the trees near his home, van Gogh wrote sad letters to his brother Theo.

■ He _____composed_____ works of great beauty that were not appreciated until after his death. Today his paintings are in museums all over the world and are sold for millions of dollars.

SIRENS IN THE NIGHT

■ When a power blackout darkened part of the city, some criminals roamed the streets. They broke windows and _____looted_____ neighborhood stores.

■ Community leaders spoke out against this _____senseless_____ violence and urged people to act responsibly during the emergency.

■ Several sheriff's _____deputies_____ arrived to restore order and interview witnesses to the crime spree.

■ One witness offered information about the robberies, but the police officers paid him little mind because they knew he was not _____reliable_____.

 **Word Associations**

*Circle the letter next to the word or expression that best completes the sentence or answers the question. Pay special attention to the word in **boldface**.*

1. Which is a **barrier** to success in school?
   a. poor study habits
   b. weak stomach muscles
   c. a tall fence
   d. no brothers or sisters

2. An **industrious** person could
   a. build a hen house in ten years
   b. build a dollhouse in five years
   c. build a birdhouse in one year
   d. build a doghouse in one day

3. A **deputy** would probably carry
   a. a badge
   b. a bag lunch
   c. a wrench
   d. a banner

4. It is **senseless** to try to count
   a. to one thousand
   b. change after a purchase
   c. grains of sand at the beach
   d. people ahead of you in line

5. You might **rejoice** if you
   a. found your lost dog
   b. ruined your favorite shirt
   c. failed a spelling test
   d. saw the latest comedy film

6. Which is a **considerable** sum?
   a. 30¢
   b. $1.00
   c. $5.00
   d. $5,000.00

7. If you **compose** your autobiography, you will be
   a. driving a new car
   b. writing the story of your life
   c. interviewing strangers
   d. making up a new song

8. You might feel **jolted** by
   a. a good night's sleep
   b. a delicious lunch
   c. shocking news
   d. yesterday's paper

9. People guilty of **looting** are
   a. winning a prize
   b. breaking the law
   c. running in circles
   d. taking pictures

10. A balloon would quickly **shrivel**
    a. if air leaks from it
    b. if it floats away
    c. if it gets wet
    d. if it is tied to a string

11. A **reliable** friend is one who
    a. doesn't let you down
    b. makes fun of you
    c. is never on time
    d. always makes you laugh

12. Which might be used to **calculate**?
    a. an alarm clock
    b. paper and pencil
    c. a hammer
    d. knife and fork

Definitions

Study the spelling, pronunciation, part of speech, and definition given for each of the words below. Write the word in the blank space in the sentence that follows. Then read the synonyms and antonyms.

1. **alternate**
   (v., ôl′ tər nāt;
   n., adj., ôl′ tər nət)

   (v.) to do, use, or happen in successive turns; to take turns
   We chose two students to _____alternate_____ in the lead role for our class play.

   (n.) a person acting or prepared to act in place of another; a substitute
   Juries usually include two or more _____alternates_____.

   (adj.) happening or appearing in turns; every other; being a choice between two or more things
   The bus driver took an _____alternate_____ route.

   SYNONYMS: (v.) to rotate, change; (n.) a replacement, deputy

2. **demolish**
   (di mäl′ ish)

   (v.) to tear down, break to pieces
   A wrecking crew arrived to _____demolish_____ the old building.

   SYNONYMS: to raze, destroy, wreck, smash, level
   ANTONYMS: to construct, build, restore, mend

3. **energetic**
   (e nər je′ tik)

   (adj.) active and vigorous, full of energy, forceful
   Our teacher has an _____energetic_____ assistant.

   SYNONYMS: hardworking, tireless, peppy
   ANTONYMS: idle, lazy, inactive

4. **enforce**
   (en fôrs′)

   (v.) to force obedience to
   It is the duty of the police to protect citizens and _____enforce_____ the laws.

   SYNONYM: to carry out
   ANTONYMS: to overlook, abandon, disregard

5. **feat**
   (fēt)

   (n.) an act or deed that shows daring, skill, or strength
   The crowd cheered when the circus strongman performed a mighty _____feat_____.

   SYNONYMS: an achievement, exploit, effort

6. **hearty**
   (härt′ ē)

   (adj.) warm and friendly; healthy, lively, and strong; large and satisfying to the appetite
   We all sat down to enjoy a _____hearty_____ meal.

   SYNONYMS: cheerful, friendly; fit, healthy; plentiful
   ANTONYMS: insincere, phony; sickly

For vocabulary games and activities, visit **www.sadlier-oxford.com**.

Sometimes explosives are used to **demolish** (word 2) structures. Here an old hotel is brought down in Atlantic City, New Jersey.

7. **mature**
(mə tür')

(v.) to bring to or reach full development or growth
The puppy will _____ mature _____ over the summer.
(adj.) fully grown or developed
A field of _____ mature _____ oats waved in the breeze.
SYNONYMS: (v.) to grow, develop, age, ripen; (adj.) complete, ripe
ANTONYMS: (adj.) immature, inexperienced, raw, green

8. **observant**
(əb zûr' vənt)

(adj.) watchful, quick to notice; careful and diligent
An _____ observant _____ guard spotted the vandals.
SYNONYMS: aware, attentive, alert, sharp; dutiful, mindful
ANTONYMS: inattentive, careless

9. **primary**
(prī' mer ē)

(adj.) first in importance, first in time or order; basic, fundamental
Raising money was our _____ primary _____ order of business.
(n.) an early election that narrows the choice of candidates who will run in a final election
The challenger won the _____ primary _____ .
SYNONYMS: (adj.) highest, main, prime
ANTONYMS: (adj.) secondary, last

10. **resign**
(ri zīn')

(v.) to give up a job, an office, or a right or claim
Richard Nixon was the first President to _____ resign _____ the office.
SYNONYMS: to quit, abandon, leave, surrender

11. **strive**
(strīv)

(v.) to devote much energy or effort, try hard
You must _____ strive _____ to finish your homework on time.
SYNONYMS: to attempt, struggle, labor, slave, strain

12. **verdict**
(vûr' dikt)

(n.) the decision of a jury at the end of a trial or legal case; any decision
The jury brought in a guilty _____ verdict _____ .
SYNONYMS: a ruling, judgment, finding

63

Match the Meaning

For each item below, choose the word whose meaning is suggested by the clue given. Then write the word in the space provided.

1. To make people obey laws is to _____ enforce _____ those laws.
   a. enforce   b. alternate   c. demolish   d. strive

2. To break something to pieces is to _____ demolish _____ it.
   a. alternate   b. demolish   c. resign   d. mature

3. An amazing act or deed might be called a(n) _____ feat _____.
   a. feat   b. verdict   c. primary   d. alternate

4. On cold mornings, my favorite breakfast is a(n) _____ hearty _____ bowl of hot oatmeal with brown sugar, cinnamon, and walnuts.
   a. mature   b. observant   c. hearty   d. primary

5. The decision that a jury gives at the end of a trial is called the _____ verdict _____.
   a. feat   b. primary   c. alternate   d. verdict

6. If you give up a job, you _____ resign _____ from it.
   a. enforce   b. resign   c. mature   d. alternate

7. Something that is first in importance, first in time order, or first in another basic way is called _____ primary _____.
   a. primary   b. mature   c. alternate   d. energetic

8. In most games, players take turns or _____ alternate _____ moves.
   a. resign   b. demolish   c. alternate   d. enforce

9. A frisky puppy can be described as _____ energetic _____.
   a. observant   b. energetic   c. mature   d. primary

10. If you are very _____ observant _____, you'll notice the clues.
   a. primary   b. hearty   c. mature   d. observant

11. Once fruit is fully _____ mature _____, it can be harvested.
   a. energetic   b. mature   c. hearty   d. alternate

12. To try very hard is to _____ strive _____.
   a. strive   b. alternate   c. demolish   d. resign

For each item below, choose the word that is most nearly the **same** in meaning as the word or phrase in **boldface**. Then write your choice on the line provided.

1. handed down the **ruling**
   a. primary   b. feat   c. alternate   d. verdict   _____ verdict

2. a **cheerful** laugh that made his shoulders jiggle
   a. alternate   b. hearty   c. mature   d. observant   _____ hearty

3. read about the daring **achievement**
   a. feat   b. verdict   c. primary   d. alternate   _____ feat

4. packed a **replacement** camera as a backup
   a. observant   b. hearty   c. primary   d. alternate   _____ alternate

5. **abandon** the job of manager
   a. alternate   b. demolish   c. strive   d. resign   _____ resign

6. **attempt** to learn to read Japanese
   a. demolish   b. alternate   c. strive   d. resign   _____ strive

Antonyms

For each item below, choose the word that is most nearly **opposite** in meaning to the word or phrase in **boldface**. Then write your choice on the line provided.

1. **construct** a covered bridge
   a. demolish   b. strive   c. alternate   d. enforce   _____ demolish

2. **idle** workers
   a. mature   b. energetic   c. observant   d. primary   _____ energetic

3. showed an **inexperienced** outlook
   a. alternate   b. hearty   c. mature   d. primary   _____ mature

4. an **inattentive** reader
   a. alternate   b. mature   c. observant   d. hearty   _____ observant

5. **overlook** the "No Smoking" laws
   a. alternate   b. strive   c. resign   d. enforce   _____ enforce

6. a **secondary** cause of blindness
   a. hearty   b. observant   c. primary   d. energetic   _____ primary

Completing the Sentence

From the list of words on pages 62–63, choose the one that best completes each item below. Write the word in the space provided. (You may have to change the word's ending.)

From the list of words on pages 62–63

RAISING A NEW HOUSE

■ The storm so badly damaged the house that it was unsafe to live in. The owner decided to _____ **demolish** _____ it and build a new one.

■ It was quite a(n) _____ **feat** _____ to tear down the house, clear the land, and build another house in only ten weeks!

■ Two crews _____ **alternated** _____ in the building work. When one finished, the other began, so that construction went on from break of day until long after the sun went down.

■ All of the workers were encouraged to _____ **strive** _____ as hard as they could to finish the job ahead of schedule.

■ Luckily, a(n) _____ **observant** _____ worker spotted a mistake in the building plans before it caused a delay, and the house was finished on time. The worker was rewarded for his attention and diligence.

AN AFTER-SCHOOL JOB

■ My sister says that the responsibilities of a part-time job can help teens develop into more _____ **mature** _____ individuals.

■ The managers at Burger Barn, where she works after school, _____ **enforce** _____ three rules: be on time, be honest, and be polite.

■ As long as she follows those rules, the managers greet her each day with a cheerful smile and a _____ **hearty** _____ handshake.

TO THE POLLS!

■ The _____ **primary** _____ election in September decided which candidates would run for state assembly in the general election in November. In the Democratic race, two politicians challenged the two-term assemblyman for a place on the ballot.

■ All three candidates had the help of many young, _____ **energetic** _____ volunteers, who worked tirelessly to get out the vote.

■ After ballots were counted, the _____ **verdict** _____ was clear: Voters wanted the two-term assemblyman to run again.

■ However, health problems in October forced him to _____ **resign** _____ his office and pull out of the election.

Word Associations

*Circle the letter next to the word or expression that best completes the sentence or answers the question. Pay special attention to the word in **boldface**.*

1. Which is a **verdict**?
   a. "Thank you!"
   b. "Good morning!"
   c. "I told you so!"
   d. "Not guilty!"

2. If you and your sister **alternate** walking the dog, then you must
   a. do twice as much walking
   b. walk the dog every other time
   c. walk the dog two times in a row
   d. walk farther than your sister

3. Which is a firefighter's **feat**?
   a. polishing the fire trucks
   b. making daring rescues
   c. wearing waterproof boots
   d. cooking firehouse stew

4. Who would **enforce** a leash law?
   a. a scientist
   b. a weather forecaster
   c. a veterinarian
   d. a dogcatcher

5. People who **strive**
   a. give up easily
   b. always succeed
   c. do their very best
   d. prefer to be outdoors

6. Which is a **mature** animal?
   a. a sleepy puppy
   b. an old turtle
   c. a frisky kitten
   d. a new chick

7. An **energetic** performer might
   a. do three shows a day
   b. nap during intermission
   c. not answer fan mail
   d. sing softly

8. Which might be **resigned**?
   a. a greeting card
   b. a doctor's prescription
   c. a homework assignment
   d. a club membership

9. A **primary** concern is one that
   a. comes last
   b. comes too late
   c. comes first
   d. comes when you least expect it

10. Which might be **hearty**?
    a. a wink
    b. a laugh
    c. a sigh
    d. a whisper

11. If you are **observant**, you are
    a. wide awake
    b. daydreaming
    c. asleep
    d. distracted

12. Which would be the hardest to **demolish**?
    a. a snow fort
    b. a house made of cards
    c. a bookcase
    d. a dollhouse

REVIEW UNITS 5–8

For vocabulary games and activities,
visit **www.sadlier-oxford.com**.

Selecting Word Meanings

*For each of the following items, circle the choice that is most nearly the **same** in meaning as the word in **boldface**.*

1. asked him to **resign**
   a. accept   **b. quit**   c. join   d. stay

2. discovered the pirates' **loot**
   a. bones   b. weapons   c. gifts   **d. stolen goods**

3. **senseless** behavior
   a. foolish   b. polite   c. noble   d. unusual

4. welcomed the **nomads**
   a. workers   b. guests   c. relatives   **d. wanderers**

5. an **energetic** group
   a. lazy   **b. lively**   c. quiet   d. friendly

6. **calculate** the distance traveled
   a. figure   b. walk   c. question   d. write down

7. a courageous **feat**
   a. failure   b. battle   c. idea   **d. deed**

8. the **supreme** example
   a. outstanding   b. original   c. unimportant   d. personal

9. **concealed** my fears
   a. hid   b. showed   c. emphasized   d. ignored

10. explored the **vast** continent
    a. beautiful   b. frozen   c. empty   **d. huge**

11. **detected** by radar
    a. hidden   b. decided   **c. discovered**   d. photographed

12. wore **civilian** clothes
    a. new   b. military   c. party   **d. nonmilitary**

Spelling

For each item below, study the **boldface** word in which there is a blank. If a letter is missing, fill in the blank to make a correctly spelled word. If the word is already spelled correctly, leave the blank empty.

1. a **verdi_c_t** of not guilty

2. **jo__lted** by the earthquake

3. an **industri_o_us** effort

4. the aquarium's **capa_c_ity**

5. ask the **depu_t_y** mayor

6. **he__arty** applause

7. **enfor_c_e** the regulations

8. keep the **d_u_plicate**

9. an **ap_p_arent** mistake

10. the **festi_v_e** mood

11. the family's **hos__pitality**

12. **ac_c_omplish** a great deal

Antonyms

For each of the following items, circle the choice that is most nearly the **opposite** in meaning to the word in **boldface**.

1. arrived at the **barrier**
   - (a.) passage
   - b. obstacle
   - c. river
   - d. corner

2. a knife's **keen** edge
   - a. sharp
   - b. rusty
   - (c.) dull
   - d. broken

3. **demolished** the car
   - (a.) built
   - b. destroyed
   - c. sold
   - d. washed

4. showed signs of **fatigue**
   - a. surprise
   - b. exhaustion
   - c. sickness
   - (d.) energy

5. a **considerable** collection of coins
   - (a.) small
   - b. huge
   - c. valuable
   - d. private

6. the **spurting** water fountain
   - a. gushing
   - b. brand-new
   - (c.) trickling
   - d. old

7. the writer's **primary** meaning
   - a. main
   - b. hidden
   - (c.) secondary
   - d. confusing

8. **persecuted** by their neighbors
   - a. hurt
   - (b.) comforted
   - c. questioned
   - d. ignored

Vocabulary for Comprehension

*Read the following passage in which some of the words you have studied appear in **boldface**. Then answer the questions on page 71.*

America's First Female Doctor

Elizabeth Blackwell (1821–1910) didn't always enjoy medicine. But once she chose to become a doctor, she let nothing stop her. In the mid-1800s, medical schools did not accept female students. People believed then that women could never become **capable** doctors. This view made Elizabeth angry. She knew that many women would feel more at ease consulting a woman rather than a man about their health. Despite public opinion, she decided to follow her dream.

Elizabeth applied to dozens of medical schools, but she was rejected by each and every one. Refusing to be discouraged, Elizabeth made **alternate** plans for her education. She read thick medical textbooks on her own. She convinced an understanding doctor to be her private tutor. She never stopped working, and she never gave up hope.

Finally, in 1847, a small college in upstate New York admitted Elizabeth Blackwell into its medical program. When she got there, she learned that her acceptance was a joke. People treated her as an outsider. Teachers and classmates teased her. Others ignored her. But Elizabeth did not let such rude behavior keep her from **accomplishing** her goal. An **industrious** student, she went to her classes and studied hard. She earned the admiration of her fellow students.

In January 1849, Elizabeth Blackwell graduated at the head of her class. She became the first woman in the United States to receive a medical degree. At her graduation, she said, "It shall be the effort of my life to shed honor on this diploma." In so doing, she broke down the **barriers** that prevented women from practicing medicine.

Fill in the circle next to the choice that best completes the sentence or answers the question.

1. This passage is best described as a(n)
   - (a) biographical sketch
   - (b) journal entry
   - (c) autobiographical sketch
   - (d) tall tale

2. Another word for **capable** is
   - (a) able
   - (b) caring
   - (c) outspoken
   - (d) eager

3. Elizabeth Blackwell was rejected by dozens of medical schools because
   - (a) she did not have good grades
   - (b) she did not study hard enough
   - (c) it was too challenging for her
   - (d) medical schools did not accept women

4. The meaning of **alternate** in this passage is
   - (a) take turns
   - (b) a substitute
   - (c) other
   - (d) enormous

5. Another word for **accomplishing** is
   - (a) abandoning
   - (b) avoiding
   - (c) adjusting
   - (d) achieving

6. **Industrious** most nearly means
   - (a) hard working
   - (b) idle
   - (c) interested
   - (d) curious

7. In this passage, the meaning of **barriers** is
   - (a) fences
   - (b) arguments
   - (c) obstacles
   - (d) vehicles

8. Elizabeth Blackwell helped other women by
   - (a) teaching women about medicine
   - (b) specializing in women's diseases
   - (c) opening the door to the medical profession
   - (d) supporting women's colleges

9. Based on this passage, Elizabeth Blackwell can best be described as
   - (a) sensitive
   - (b) determined
   - (c) nervous
   - (d) curious

10. What can be learned from Elizabeth Blackwell?
    - (a) the need for a sense of humor
    - (b) the importance of goals
    - (c) the meaning of friendship
    - (d) the value of honor

Grammar in Context

Sometimes the subject in a sentence is a compound subject or the predicate is a compound predicate.

A **compound subject** is two or more subjects that have the same predicate. A conjunction such as *and* joins the subjects.

> <u>Teachers</u> teased her. <u>Classmates</u> teased her.
>
> <u>Teachers and classmates</u> teased her. ⟵ **compound subject**

A **compound predicate** is two or more predicates that have the same subject. A conjunction such as *and* joins the predicates.

> She <u>went to her classes</u>. She <u>studied hard</u>.
>
> She <u>went to her classes and studied hard</u>. ⟵ **compound predicate**

*Read each pair of sentences. Combine them by joining the subjects or predicates with the word **and**. Write the new sentence on the line.*

1. Elizabeth writes letters. Elizabeth composes speeches. <u>Elizabeth writes letters and composes speeches.</u>

2. The students work hard. The students strive to do their best. <u>The students work hard and strive to do their best.</u>

3. Hospitals enforce unfair rules. Clinics enforce unfair rules. <u>Hospitals and clinics enforce unfair rules.</u>

4. Students cheer for Elizabeth. Students rejoice for Elizabeth. <u>Students cheer and rejoice for Elizabeth.</u>

5. Friends cannot conceal their delight. Family cannot conceal their delight. <u>Friends and family cannot conceal their delight.</u>

*Complete each sentence so that it makes sense. Pay attention to the word in **boldface**.*

Accept answers that show an understanding of the vocabulary.

1. Dad had such a **hearty** appetite that he _____.

2. The city had to **demolish** the old house because _____.

3. I am **reliable** because I always _____.

4. Among the **loot**, the police found _____.

5. It's smart to have a **duplicate** key in case you _____.

6. It **provokes** me when you say that I _____.

7. To **transport** those heavy boxes, we can _____.

8. My favorite way to **conclude** a meal is to _____.

9. If I were a **nomad**, I'd probably _____.

10. To find the **capacity** of a fish tank, you can _____.

11. If I had a **considerable** amount of time, I would _____.

12. The most amazing **feat** I ever saw was _____.

13. I will **resign** from the team if the coach _____.

14. I feel **fatigue** when I _____.

15. To show our **hospitality**, we should _____.

Write Your Own

Choose a word from Units 5–8. Write a sentence using the word. Be sure each sentence has a subject and a predicate. If you wrote a compound subject or a compound predicate, underline it.

Check that the vocabulary is used correctly and that the sentence is written correctly.

_____

Word Families

*The words in **boldface** in the sentences below are related to words introduced in Units 5–8. For example, the nouns* festivity *and* energy *in item 1 are related to the adjectives* festive *(Unit 5) and* energetic *(Unit 8). Based on your understanding of the unit words that follow, circle the related word in **boldface** that best completes each sentence.*

accomplish	alternate	blunt	calculate	capable
compose	detect	duplicate	energetic	enforce
festive	hospitality	industrious	mature	observant
provoke	reliable	supreme	transport	undoing

1. If you are going on a long hike over steep hills on a hot summer day, you will need a lot of (**festivity**/**energy**).

2. The Environmental Protection Agency is responsible for the (**enforcement**/ **duplication**) of laws passed to ensure clean air and water for all Americans.

3. For English class I wrote a (**calculation**/**composition**) about my family's trip to the Grand Canyon.

4. Passengers on whale-watching cruises can (**observe**/**undo**) whales and sometimes dolphins swimming in the open ocean.

5. The guests at a party may talk about how (**provocative**/**hospitable**) their hosts are to everyone.

6. Today people can choose from many different kinds of (**transportation**/ **detection**) to travel across the United States and around the world.

7. A computer has the (**capability**/**maturity**) to solve complicated mathematical problems very quickly.

8. Most bosses agree that (**bluntness**/**industry**) is a valuable quality in an employee.

9. My parents chose our new family car for its (**supremacy**/**reliability**) in all kinds of weather conditions.

10. All over the world people gather in front of television sets to watch the amazing (**accomplishments**/**alternatives**) of athletes at the Olympic Games.

Go for the Gold! Find and ring the ten words from Units 5–8 that are hidden in the grid below. Then choose from these words the ones that best complete the sentences that follow. Write the words in the blanks.

S	R	E	L	I	A	B	L	E	N
T	O	P	O	S	B	L	E	M	O
R	C	C	O	N	C	E	A	L	M
I	K	O	T	K	I	M	S	T	A
V	E	N	V	L	U	I	E	A	D
E	T	C	R	O	V	S	B	W	E
A	L	L	W	N	Y	H	E	R	O
S	P	U	R	T	V	O	T	E	R
Z	O	D	U	O	F	F	E	A	T
K	E	E	N	N	D	G	Q	T	O

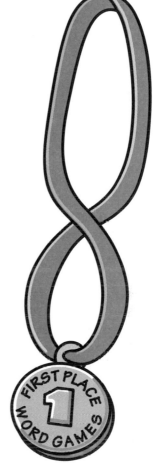

Countries from every continent send their finest and most _____reliable_____ athletes to compete in the Olympic Games.

All the athletes who take part in the games _____strive_____ to do their very best for their countries, their teams, and themselves.

People all over the world watch the games with _____keen_____ interest.

Some athletes achieve the remarkable _____feat_____ of setting new world records.

Many athletes, such as speed skaters and marathon runners, may rely on an extra _____spurt_____ of energy at the finish of their races.

By tradition, the marathon is run on the day that the Games _____conclude_____.

Definitions — *Choose the word from the box that matches each definition. Write the word on the line provided. The first one has been done for you.*

alternate	apparent	barrier	blemish	blunder
capable	considerable	duplicate	feat	glamour
impressive	luxurious	miniature	persecute	solitary
scuffle	straggle	~~transport~~	undoing	verdict

1. to move or carry from one place to another   <u>transport</u>

2. a mark or stain that damages the appearance   <u>blemish</u>

3. fairly large in size or extent   <u>considerable</u>

4. to stray off or trail behind   <u>straggle</u>

5. living or being alone; being the only one   <u>solitary</u>

6. mysterious charm, beauty, or attractiveness   <u>glamour</u>

7. having a strong effect, commanding attention   <u>impressive</u>

8. a bringing to ruin; the cause of ruin   <u>undoing</u>

9. to copy exactly; to produce something equal to   <u>duplicate</u>

10. to make a foolish or careless mistake   <u>blunder</u>

11. the decision of a jury at the end of a trial   <u>verdict</u>

12. to take turns   <u>alternate</u>

13. able and prepared to do something; fit or skilled   <u>capable</u>

14. open to view; seeming to be true or real   <u>apparent</u>

15. a very small copy, model, or painting   <u>miniature</u>

Antonyms

*Choose the word from the box that is most nearly **opposite** in meaning to each group of words. Write the word on the line provided. The first one has been done for you.*

1. a rival, foe, enemy	associate	accomplish
2. sad, gloomy, somber	festive	aggressive
3. to accept, receive, take	reject	assault
4. inexperienced, raw, green	veteran	~~associate~~
5. to reveal, uncover	conceal	cautious
6. to grieve, mourn	rejoice	conceal
7. daring, reckless, wild	cautious	conclude
8. lasting, long-lived, permanent	temporary	despise
9. shy, bashful, retiring	aggressive	dispute
10. to begin, start, open	conclude	energetic
11. a hero, heroine, champion	villain	festive
12. idle, lazy, inactive	energetic	fragile
13. to defend, protect, resist	assault	haven
14. to hurry, rush, hasten	linger	justify
15. tiny, small, little	vast	linger
16. sturdy, hardy, strong	fragile	mature
17. to admire, esteem, adore	despise	reject
18. to expand, enlarge, swell	shrivel	rejoice
19. faithful, trustworthy; safe	treacherous	senseless
20. to agree; an agreement	dispute	shrivel
		temporary
		treacherous
		vast
		veteran
		villain

Completing the Sentence

Choose the word from the box that best completes each sentence below. Write the word in the space provided. The first one has been done for you.

Group A

blunt	civilian	emigrate	hearty
hospitality	industrious	~~myth~~	resign

1. I enjoyed reading the story of Demeter and Persephone, a Greek _____myth_____ that explains summer and winter.

2. Are you familiar with Aesop's fable about the lazy grasshopper and the _____industrious_____ ant?

3. My cousins in Eastern Europe hope to _____emigrate_____ to the United States and join the rest of the family here.

4. I wrote a note to thank you for your gracious _____hospitality_____ last weekend.

5. Let's give a(n) _____hearty_____ welcome to our guests who have traveled so far to be with us!

Group B

cancel	compose	hazy	obstacle
reliable	strategy	vivid	withdraw

1. Before asking Mom to increase our allowance, we'll plan a(n) _____strategy_____ that is sure to succeed.

2. After Dad painted the car a(n) _____vivid_____ shade of green, it was easy to spot in a crowded parking lot.

3. I plan to pay you as soon as I _____withdraw_____ the money from the bank.

4. I have only a(n) _____hazy_____ idea of what I will do during summer vacation.

5. Let's work together to _____compose_____ lyrics for a new school song.

Classifying

Choose the word from the box that goes best with each group of words. Write the word in the space provided. Then explain what the words have in common. The first one has been done for you.

capacity	~~continuous~~	convert	detect	flexible
loot	monarch	nomad	numerous	primary

1. ongoing, endless, _____ continuous _____

   The words are synonyms.

2. _____ convert _____, conversion, convertible

   The words belong to the same family.

3. some, a few, many, _____ numerous _____

   The words describe amounts.

4. president, dictator, _____ monarch _____

   The words name heads of government.

5. bendable, adjustable, _____ flexible _____

   The words are synonyms.

6. _____ detect _____, detective, detector

   The words belong to the same family.

7. tribe, camel, tent, _____ nomad _____

   The words relate to a way of life.

8. length, weight, _____ capacity _____

   The words name attributes that can be measured.

9. boot, root, hoot, _____ loot _____

   The words rhyme.

10. _____ primary _____, middle, secondary

   The words describe levels of school.

Analogies

In each of the following, circle the letter for the item that best completes the comparison. Then explain the relationship on the lines provided. The first one has been done for you.

1. **cautious** is to **careful** as
   a. numerous is to simple
   b. continuous is to ugly
   c. aggressive is to forceful
   d. misleading is to true

   Relationship: "Cautious" and "careful" are synonyms; "aggressive" and "forceful" are synonyms.

2. **shrewd** is to **foolish** as
   a. high is to towering
   b. happy is to sad
   c. spotless is to neat
   d. famous is to rich

   Relationship: "Shrewd" and "foolish" are opposites/antonyms; "happy" and "sad" are opposites/antonyms.

3. **passport** is to **document** as
   a. step is to scuffle
   b. punch is to assault
   c. map is to strategy
   d. discussion is to dispute

   Relationship: A "passport" is a type of "document"; a "punch" is a type of "assault."

4. **mistake** is to **blunder** as
   a. obstacle is to opening
   b. glamour is to wealth
   c. myth is to history
   d. outlaw is to villain

   Relationship: "Mistake" and "blunder" are synonyms; "outlaw" and "villain" are synonyms.

5. **monarch** is to **kingdom** as
   a. veteran is to war
   b. villain is to hero
   c. mayor is to city
   d. senator is to election

   Relationship: A "monarch" governs a "kingdom"; a "mayor" governs a "city."

6. **flexible** is to **bend** as
   a. productive is to hinder
   b. hazy is to burn
   c. fragile is to break
   d. temporary is to dissolve

   Relationship: Something "flexible" can "bend"; something "fragile" can "break."

7. **dependable** is to **reliable** as
   a. hearty is to sickly
   b. dry is to moist
   c. round is to circular *(circled)*
   d. logical is to senseless

Relationship: <u>"Dependable" and "reliable"</u> <u>are synonyms; "round" and "circular" are</u> <u>synonyms.</u>

9. **apparent** is to **obvious** as
   a. first is to primary *(circled)*
   b. dull is to keen
   c. early is to late
   d. mature is to immature

Relationship: <u>"Apparent" and "obvious" are</u> <u>synonyms; "first" and "primary" are</u> <u>synonyms.</u>

8. **begin** is to **conclude** as
   a. search is to look
   b. help is to aid
   c. remain is to stay
   d. give up is to strive *(circled)*

Relationship: <u>"Begin" and "conclude" are</u> <u>antonyms; "give up" and "strive" are</u> <u>antonyms.</u>

10. **celebration** is to **rejoice** as
   a. library is to shout
   b. contest is to compete *(circled)*
   c. feast is to starve
   d. building is to demolish

Relationship: <u>One would "rejoice" at a</u> <u>"celebration"; one would "compete" in a</u> <u>"contest."</u>

Challenge: Make up your own

Write a comparison using the words in the box below. (Hint: There are three possible analogies.) Then explain the relationship on the lines provided.

barracks	barrier	blemish	blunt
civilian	club	flaw	home
keen	obstacle	soldier	sword

A possible answer is given.

Analogy: <u>flaw</u> is to <u>blemish</u> as <u>barrier</u> is to <u>obstacle</u>.

Relationship: <u>"Flaw" and "blemish" are synonyms; "barrier" and "obstacle" are synonyms.</u>

Building with Latin and Greek Roots

A **root** is the basic part of a word. Knowing the meanings of common word roots can often help you figure out the meanings of words with those roots.

> **port**—carry
>
> The root **port** appears in **transport**. When you **transport** something, you move or carry it from one place to another.

*The words below contain the root **port**. Study the definition of each word. Then write the word on the line in the sample sentence.*

1. **import**   to bring goods or materials into one country from another

    Many countries ——————— import ——————— bananas from Costa Rica.

2. **portage**   the carrying of boats or goods over land from one body of water to another

    ——————— Portage ——————— of the supplies around the lake took over a day.

3. **porter**   someone whose job it is to carry bags or other loads, as at a railroad station or in a hotel

    The ——————— porter ——————— loaded my heavy suitcase onto the train.

4. **portfolio**   a carrying case for loose papers or drawings; briefcase

    The student brings his artwork to class in a waterproof ——————— portfolio ———————.

5. **support**   to hold up; to keep from falling; to provide for; to back or uphold

    We donate money to ——————— support ——————— the Wildlife Center.

*Circle the word in **boldface** that best completes each sentence.*

1. This beautifully written essay ought to be put in your writing
   (**portage,** **portfolio**).

2. Wooden posts (**import,** **support**) the deck in our yard.

3. From which country do we (**import,** **support**) the most electronic games?

4. My grandfather worked as a (**porter,** **portfolio**) on the Union
   Pacific Railway.

5. The 10-mile (**portage,** **porter**) between rivers took longer than expected.

*From the list of words on page 82, choose the one that best completes
each sentence below. Write the word on the line provided.*

1. My mother works two jobs to
   _____support_____ our family.

2. She brought along a _____portfolio_____
   with samples of her poetry.

3. It is customary to tip the
   _____porter_____ who
   helps you with your suitcases.

4. The gift shops _____import_____
   unique handmade pottery from Mexico.

5. For the first _____portage_____, the
   canoe was hauled along a 1-mile path.

Definitions

Study the spelling, pronunciation, part of speech, and definition given for each of the words below. Write the word in the blank space in the sentence that follows. Then read the synonyms and antonyms.

1. **brisk**
   (brisk)

   (adj.) energetic, lively, fast; cool and fresh
   The flag snapped and fluttered in the _____brisk_____ *wind.*

   SYNONYMS: quick, active, peppy; refreshing, nippy
   ANTONYMS: slow, dull, sluggish

2. **cherish**
   (cher′ ish)

   (v.) to feel or show great love for; to value highly; to take special care of
   Our freedom is something we should always safeguard and _____cherish_____.

   SYNONYMS: to treasure, hold dear, honor; to prize, preserve
   ANTONYMS: to hate, despise, dishonor; to neglect

3. **considerate**
   (kən si′ də rət)

   (adj.) showing concern for the needs or feelings of others
   If you are a _____considerate_____ *guest, you might be invited back.*

   SYNONYMS: thoughtful, kind, giving, gracious
   ANTONYMS: thoughtless, self-centered, selfish

4. **displace**
   (dis plās′)

   (v.) to force to move or flee; to move out of position
   Officials feared that the flood would _____displace_____ *the villagers from their homes.*

   SYNONYMS: to uproot, expel, evict, dislodge
   ANTONYMS: to settle, plant, install

5. **downfall**
   (daún′ fôl)

   (n.) a sudden fall from power or position; a sudden and heavy snow or rain
   To this day, historians argue over what caused the Roman empire's _____downfall_____.

   SYNONYMS: collapse, ruin
   ANTONYMS: triumph, success

6. **estimate**
   (*v.*, es′ tə māt;
   n., es′ tə mət)

   (v.) to form a rough judgment about the size, quantity, or value of something
   I would _____estimate_____ *the number of people at the concert at about 15,000.*

   (n.) a rough calculation; a careful guess
   The mechanic gave us an _____estimate_____ *for the cost of the repairs.*

   SYNONYMS: (v.) to figure, judge; (n.) a calculation, opinion

Internet For vocabulary games and activities, visit **www.sadlier-oxford.com**.

Fraternal twins may not look very much alike. But twins who are **identical** (word 8), like those pictured here, are usually very hard to tell apart.

7. **humiliate**
(hyü mi′ lē āt)

(v.) to hurt someone's self-respect or pride
Our opponents accused us of trying to _____humiliate_____ *them by running up the score.*

SYNONYMS: to shame, disgrace, dishonor, embarrass
ANTONYMS: to honor, applaud, praise

8. **identical**
(ī den′ ti kəl)

(adj.) exactly the same, alike in every way
The twins liked to wear _____identical_____ *outfits.*

SYNONYM: matching
ANTONYMS: unlike, different, opposite

9. **improper**
(im prä′ pər)

(adj.) not correct; showing bad manners or taste
The principal reminded us that _____improper_____ *behavior is not acceptable.*

SYNONYMS: incorrect, wrong; impolite, unsuitable, rude
ANTONYMS: proper, right; appropriate, polite

10. **poll**
(pōl)

(n.) a collecting of votes; (*usually plural*) a place where voting takes place; a collecting of opinions
Where did you see the results of the _____poll_____*?*

(v.) to receive votes; to vote; to question people to collect opinions
We are going to _____poll_____ *fifth graders about their favorite movies.*

SYNONYMS: (n.) an election; a survey, tally; (v.) to interview, tally up

11. **soothe**
(süth)

(v.) to make calm; to ease pain or sorrow
A nurse tried to _____soothe_____ *the fussy child.*

SYNONYMS: to quiet, pacify; to comfort, relieve
ANTONYMS: to excite, upset; to hurt, worsen

12. **vicinity**
(və si′ nə tē)

(n.) the area near a place, the surrounding region
There is a park in the _____vicinity_____ *of our school.*

SYNONYMS: neighborhood, area, surroundings

Match the Meaning

For each item below, choose the word whose meaning is suggested by the clue given. Then write the word in the space provided.

1. Things that look exactly alike are said to be _____identical_____.
   a. brisk   b. improper   c. identical   d. considerate

2. A heavy snowstorm would produce a(n) _____downfall_____.
   a. estimate   b. poll   c. vicinity   d. downfall

3. To make an injury less painful is to _____soothe_____ it.
   a. soothe   b. humiliate   c. displace   d. cherish

4. A grocery store in your neighborhood is in the _____vicinity_____ of your home.
   a. poll   b. vicinity   c. downfall   d. estimate

5. A cool, breezy morning might be described as _____brisk_____.
   a. considerate   b. identical   c. improper   d. brisk

6. A person who is thoughtful of the feelings of others is said to be _____considerate_____.
   a. considerate   b. improper   c. identical   d. brisk

7. To learn the opinions of consumers, you might _____poll_____ them.
   a. cherish   b. poll   c. displace   d. estimate

8. To take special care of something is to _____cherish_____ it.
   a. poll   b. estimate   c. displace   d. cherish

9. A rough calculation is also called a(n) _____estimate_____.
   a. vicinity   b. downfall   c. estimate   d. poll

10. To move something aside is to _____displace_____ it.
    a. estimate   b. displace   c. soothe   d. humiliate

11. Rude behavior might be criticized as _____improper_____.
    a. brisk   b. improper   c. considerate   d. identical

12. To embarrass or disgrace someone is to _____humiliate_____ that person.
    a. poll   b. soothe   c. cherish   d. humiliate

Synonyms

*For each item below, choose the word that is most nearly the **same** in meaning as the word or phrase in **boldface**. Then write your choice on the line provided.*

1. **dislodged** by the earthquake
   a. cherished   b. displaced   c. polled   d. soothed   _____ displaced _____

2. **embarrassed** by a failing grade
   a. cherished   b. soothed   c. humiliated   d. displaced   _____ humiliated _____

3. **treasure** the memory of my first home run
   a. estimate   b. poll   c. cherish   d. humiliate   _____ cherish _____

4. **survey** voters on their choice for senator
   a. soothe   b. estimate   c. poll   d. humiliate   _____ poll _____

5. recommended a restaurant in the **area**
   a. downfall   b. vicinity   c. poll   d. estimate   _____ vicinity _____

6. **judged** the distance to be thirty feet
   a. polled   b. estimated   c. cherished   d. humiliated   _____ estimated _____

Antonyms

*For each item below, choose the word that is most nearly **opposite** in meaning to the word or phrase in **boldface**. Then write your choice on the line provided.*

1. the general's **triumph**
   a. downfall   b. estimate   c. poll   d. vicinity   _____ downfall _____

2. set a **slow** pace
   a. identical   b. brisk   c. improper   d. considerate   _____ brisk _____

3. held **different** views
   a. improper   b. brisk   c. identical   d. considerate   _____ identical _____

4. truly **thoughtless** behavior
   a. considerate   b. brisk   c. identical   d. improper   _____ considerate _____

5. **worsened** the pain
   a. humiliated   b. estimated   c. polled   d. soothed   _____ soothed _____

6. **correct** use of the word
   a. brisk   b. considerate   c. improper   d. identical   _____ improper _____

Completing the Sentence

From the list of words on pages 84–85, choose the one that best completes each item below. Then write the word in the blank space provided. (You may have to change the word's ending.)

A POLITICAL CHARGE BACKFIRES

■ In a heated speech late in the campaign, the mayor's opponent accused her of the _____**improper**_____ use of public funds. The mayor immediately denied the charge, declaring that she had never personally profited from her office.

■ A local newspaper conducted a _____**poll**_____ of likely voters. The results showed that more than 75% of those surveyed did not believe the charge leveled against the mayor.

■ Rather than be _____**humiliated**_____ by what would almost certainly be a lopsided defeat, her opponent pulled out of the race. The mayor went on to win the election by a landslide.

THE BUFFALO TRAIL

■ Before they were forcibly _____**displaced**_____ by federal troops and European settlers, hundreds of thousands of Native Americans dwelled on the Great Plains. Among these tribes were the Blackfeet, Crow, and Sioux.

■ _____**Brisk**_____ autumn winds and deep winter snows made warm clothing and shelter essential to survival on the Great Plains. Some of these robes and the tents were made from buffalo hides.

■ Because they were so dependent upon the buffalo for food as well, many tribes never strayed very far from the _____**vicinity**_____ of the huge herds that grazed the prairie.

■ Experts _____**estimate**_____ that as many as 30 million buffalo once roamed the vast open stretches of the northern Plains.

■ The Great Plains tribes _____**cherished**_____ their traditions and way of life. To dishonor these customs was a serious offense.

■ The destruction of the buffalo herds in the late 1800s was one of the factors that led to the _____**downfall**_____ of these tribes.

A FRIEND'S GOOD TURN

■ I was very upset to learn that a friend planned to come to the party in a costume _____**identical**_____ to mine.

■ To _____**soothe**_____ my hurt feelings, she offered to wear a different costume instead.

■ It was very _____**considerate**_____ of her to do that for me, don't you think?

*Circle the letter next to the word or expression that best completes the sentence or answers the question. Pay special attention to the word in **boldface**.*

1. Which of the following would you use after a **downfall**?
   a. a watering can
   b. a rake
   c. a snow shovel
   d. a hoe

2. To be **humiliated** would make you
   a. feel happy
   b. feel intelligent
   c. feel confident
   d. feel ashamed

3. If you **cherish** your pets, you
   a. will take good care of them
   b. will forget them
   c. will mistreat them
   d. will sell them

4. Which could you easily **estimate**?
   a. the height of your desk
   b. the number of seconds in a day
   c. the distance to Pluto
   d. the cost of a jumbo jet

5. Which can be **identical**?
   a. snowflakes
   b. twins
   c. fingerprints
   d. planets

6. What does one do at the **polls**?
   a. sleep
   b. learn
   c. eat
   d. vote

7. If water is **displaced**,
   a. it might freeze
   b. it might boil
   c. it might evaporate
   d. it might spill

8. For **improper** conduct, I would be
   a. scolded
   b. rewarded
   c. praised
   d. ignored

9. Which would you wear when the weather is **brisk**?
   a. a bathing suit
   b. sandals
   c. a sweater
   d. a watch

10. A **considerate** person
    a. is usually late
    b. is a poor loser
    c. is rich and famous
    d. is thoughtful of others

11. Which might be used to **soothe**?
    a. sandpaper
    b. lotion
    c. dynamite
    d. gasoline

12. In the **vicinity** of your face is
    a. your nose
    b. your toe
    c. your knee
    d. your elbow

Unit 9 ■ *89*

Definitions

Study the spelling, pronunciation, part of speech, and definition given for each of the words below. Write the word in the blank space in the sentence that follows. Then read the synonyms and antonyms.

1. **abolish**
   (ə bä' lish)

   (v.) to do away completely with something; put an end to
   Will human beings ever be able to _____abolish_____ war?

   SYNONYMS: to outlaw, ban, repeal, stamp out
   ANTONYMS: to establish, restore

2. **appeal**
   (ə pēl')

   (n.) a sincere or strong request for something that is needed; a quality or ability that attracts or interests people; a request to a higher court for review of a legal decision
   Some people don't understand the _____appeal_____ of video games.

   (v.) to ask strongly for help, understanding, or something else needed; to be attractive or interesting; to request review of a legal decision
   Our class will _____appeal_____ for aid for the homeless.

   SYNONYMS: (n.) a plea, petition; charm, attraction; (v.) to plead, implore, beg
   ANTONYMS: (v.) to repel, disgust, repulse

3. **brittle**
   (bri' təl)

   (adj.) easily broken, snapped, or cracked; not flexible
   The pages of the old book had turned _____brittle_____.

   SYNONYMS: breakable, stiff, unbending, fragile
   ANTONYMS: bendable, flexible, elastic, rugged

4. **condemn**
   (kən dem')

   (v.) to criticize a person or action as wrong, guilty, or evil; to judge as guilty and to punish
   The judge is expected to _____condemn_____ the defendant to life imprisonment.

   SYNONYMS: to disapprove, denounce, blame
   ANTONYMS: to praise, admire, honor, applaud, approve

5. **descend**
   (di send')

   (v.) to move to a lower place from a higher one; to come or be handed down from the past
   We watched the climber _____descend_____ the cliff.

   SYNONYMS: to drop, fall, plunge, climb down; to stem, derive
   ANTONYMS: to rise, climb, scale, ascend

6. **dictator**
   (dik' tā tər)

   (n.) a ruler or leader who has total power
   Sometimes my older brother acts like a _____dictator_____.

   SYNONYMS: tyrant, master, despot, oppressor

Frederick Douglass was an escaped slave who became a leader in
the movement to **abolish** (word 1) slavery. His autobiography
has become a classic of American literature.

7. **expand**
(ik spand')

(v.) to open up, make or grow larger; to develop
The principal plans to _____ expand _____ our classroom.

SYNONYMS: to spread, stretch, swell, enlarge
ANTONYMS: to shrink, reduce, contract, abridge

8. **famine**
(fa' mən)

(n.) a severe shortage of food over a large area
Children especially suffered during the _____ famine _____.

SYNONYMS: hunger, starvation, scarcity, want
ANTONYMS: feast, plenty

9. **portable**
(pôr' tə bəl)

(adj.) easily moved or carried
Dad put a _____ portable _____ crib in the trunk.

SYNONYMS: movable, transportable
ANTONYMS: immovable, fixed, rooted

10. **prey**
(prā)

(n.) an animal hunted as food by another; someone or something that
is helpless against attack
The documentary showed a lion stalking its _____ prey _____.

(v.) (used with *on* or *upon*) to hunt for food; to harm, rob, or take
advantage of
Only a bully would _____ prey _____ upon the weak.

SYNONYMS: (n.) a victim; quarry; (v.) to devour; to bully, victimize, cheat
ANTONYMS: (n.) a hunter, predator

11. **thrifty**
(thrif' tē)

(adj.) careful about spending money; tending to save money;
managing money well
My parents are teaching me to be a _____ thrifty _____ shopper.

SYNONYMS: economical, frugal, tightfisted
ANTONYMS: wasteful, careless, extravagant

12. **visual**
(vi' zhə wəl)

(adj.) having to do with sight or seeing
The math teacher likes to use _____ visual _____ aids.

SYNONYMS: visible, pictured, shown, illustrated

For each item below, choose the word whose meaning is suggested by the clue given. Then write the word in the space provided.

1. To judge an action as wrong is to _____ condemn _____ it.
   a. condemn   b. descend   c. expand   d. abolish

2. New rooms will _____ expand _____ the museum's exhibit space.
   a. condemn   b. expand   c. abolish   d. descend

3. Something that is hunted is called _____ prey _____.
   a. dictator   b. famine   c. appeal   d. prey

4. An object that you can pick up and carry with you could be described as _____ portable _____.
   a. brittle   b. visual   c. portable   d. thrifty

5. A serious food shortage might cause a(n) _____ famine _____.
   a. prey   b. appeal   c. dictator   d. famine

6. To put an end to something is to _____ abolish _____ it.
   a. appeal   b. abolish   c. descend   d. expand

7. Something that attracts is said to have _____ appeal _____.
   a. appeal   b. famine   c. dictator   d. prey

8. A ruler who does not share power is a(n) _____ dictator _____.
   a. appeal   b. prey   c. dictator   d. famine

9. An object that snaps easily is said to be _____ brittle _____.
   a. visual   b. brittle   c. portable   d. thrifty

10. A _____ visual _____ experience is one that has to do with sight or seeing.
    a. brittle   b. portable   c. thrifty   d. visual

11. To move downward is to _____ descend _____.
    a. expand   b. descend   c. abolish   d. condemn

12. A person who looks for bargains is _____ thrifty _____.
    a. thrifty   b. portable   c. visual   d. brittle

Synonyms

*For each item below, choose the word that is most nearly the **same** in meaning as the word or phrase in **boldface**. Then write your choice on the line provided.*

1. a **movable** television
   a. brittle   b. portable   c. thrifty   d. visual   _____ portable _____

2. reported on the terrible **scarcity**
   a. appeal   b. prey   c. dictator   d. famine   _____ famine _____

3. a powerful and selfish **tyrant**
   a. prey   b. famine   c. appeal   d. dictator   _____ dictator _____

4. **plead** for help
   a. abolish   b. descend   c. appeal   d. prey   _____ appeal _____

5. **visible** proof of the break-in
   a. visual   b. brittle   c. thrifty   d. portable   _____ visual _____

6. turned **stiff** by the cold
   a. brittle   b. visual   c. portable   d. thrifty   _____ brittle _____

Antonyms

*For each item below, choose the word that is most nearly **opposite** in meaning to the word or phrase in **boldface**. Then write your choice on the line provided.*

1. **shrink** the size of the project
   a. expand   b. descend   c. appeal   d. condemn   _____ expand _____

2. tracked the **predator**
   a. dictator   b. prey   c. appeal   d. famine   _____ prey _____

3. **restore** the tax on medicine
   a. condemn   b. descend   c. abolish   d. expand   _____ abolish _____

4. **praised** the decision
   a. appealed   b. descended   c. abolished   d. condemned   _____ condemned _____

5. a **wasteful** consumer
   a. portable   b. visual   c. thrifty   d. brittle   _____ thrifty _____

6. **ascend** the mountain
   a. prey upon   b. descend   c. abolish   d. expand   _____ descend _____

Completing the Sentence

From the list of words on pages 90–91, choose the one that best completes each item below. Write the word in the space provided. (You may have to change the word's ending.)

AN END TO SLAVERY

■ Before the Civil War, many northerners _____condemned_____ slavery as a terrible evil, but few wanted to go to war because of it. Abraham Lincoln, too, personally hated slavery but was prepared to accept it if by doing so the Union could be preserved.

■ Once the war began, however, many in the north argued that the time had come to _____abolish_____ slavery once and for all. In 1863 Lincoln issued the Emancipation Proclamation, freeing slaves in the states of the Confederacy.

■ Abraham Lincoln's enemies called him a(n) _____dictator_____ because he exercised so much power during the war.

■ Illustrators and photographers accompanied Union troops during some of the war's bloodiest campaigns, leaving us an important _____visual_____ record of the horrors experienced by the soldiers on both sides of the conflict.

■ Some African Americans who have _____descended_____ from slave families have passed along dramatic stories of their ancestors' experiences.

DROUGHT LEADS TO HUNGER

■ Without enough water, plant fibers dry out and become _____brittle_____. If a drought lasts for a long time, plants and crops die.

■ If too many plants die, insects have no food, and the birds and animals that _____prey_____ on insects then lose their food supply, too.

■ The threat of _____famine_____ often drives animals great distances in search of food.

■ If these animals do not _____expand_____ their hunting area, they too will starve.

A TEACHER ON A BUDGET

■ It would help our teacher a lot to have a _____portable_____ computer that she could take back and forth between school and her home.

■ She has asked businesses to donate any equipment that they no longer need. So far, more than a dozen businesses have answered her _____appeal_____ with computers and monitors for our classroom.

■ It has been a very _____thrifty_____ way of modernizing our classroom because it has cost hardly anything at all.

Word Associations

*Circle the letter next to the word or expression that best completes the sentence or answers the question. Pay special attention to the word in **boldface**.*

1. A **dictator** is most likely
   a. to be loved
   b. to be honored
   c. to be elected
   d. to be feared

2. If a book **appeals** to you,
   a. you will probably read it
   b. it is probably very long
   c. it is probably boring
   d. you will never read it

3. Which would most likely be **condemned**?
   a. promptness
   b. cruelty
   c. generosity
   d. kindness

4. A **thrifty** person would
   a. give all of her money away
   b. never buy anything on sale
   c. count every penny
   d. leave a generous tip

5. If a rule is **abolished**,
   a. it must be obeyed
   b. it is in effect only one day
   c. it is no longer in effect
   d. it lasts forever

6. Which is a **visual** aid?
   a. a cane
   b. a set of false teeth
   c. a crutch
   d. a pair of glasses

7. If a **famine** struck,
   a. water would be scarce
   b. food would be scarce
   c. money would be scarce
   d. gasoline would be scarce

8. Which is a bird of **prey**?
   a. a canary
   b. a robin
   c. a hummingbird
   d. a hawk

9. Which might you **descend**?
   a. a ladder
   b. a lake
   c. a lily
   d. a lasso

10. If my waistline **expands**, I get
   a. taller
   b. bigger around the middle
   c. shorter
   d. smaller around the middle

11. If something is **brittle**,
   a. it breaks easily
   b. it freezes quickly
   c. it is hard to see
   d. it is easy to carry

12. Which type of house is meant to be **portable**?
   a. a 15-room mansion
   b. a house trailer
   c. a log cabin
   d. a schoolhouse

UNIT 11

Definitions

Study the spelling, pronunciation, part of speech, and definition given for each of the words below. Write the word in the blank space in the sentence that follows. Then read the synonyms and antonyms.

1. **absurd**
   (əb sûrd')

   (adj.) making no sense at all, going completely against or having no reason

   No one is going to believe such an _____absurd_____ *story!*

   SYNONYMS: silly, ridiculous, foolish, crazy, insane
   ANTONYMS: sensible, wise, intelligent, sound

2. **avalanche**
   (a' və lanch)

   (n.) a large mass of snow, ice, rocks, or other material sliding or falling swiftly down a mountainside; something resembling such an event

   The skiers were almost buried by an _____avalanche_____ *that came roaring down the slope.*

   SYNONYMS: a landslide, flood, cascade

3. **classify**
   (kla' sə fī)

   (v.) to group or label in an organized way

   Libraries usually _____classify_____ *books by title, author, and subject.*

   SYNONYMS: to order, arrange, sort, catalog, pigeonhole

4. **ensure**
   (en shûr')

   (v.) to make sure, safe, or certain; to guarantee

   The playground was designed to _____ensure_____ *the children's safety.*

   SYNONYMS: to confirm, insure
   ANTONYMS: to risk, endanger

5. **navigate**
   (na' və gāt)

   (v.) to plan and steer the course of a vessel or vehicle; to make one's way, get around

   A pilot came aboard to _____navigate_____ *the steamboat down the river.*

   SYNONYMS: to guide, pilot, operate

6. **nestle**
   (ne' səl)

   (v.) to settle down comfortably; to hold lovingly

   When I was little, I liked to _____nestle_____ *in my grandmother's lap.*

   SYNONYMS: to cuddle, snuggle

A pilot uses charts and instruments to **navigate** (word 5) a helicopter.

7. **plea**
   (plē)

   (n.) an urgent request for help; the answer given in a law court by a person accused of a crime

   The defendant entered a _____ plea _____ of not guilty.

   SYNONYMS: an appeal, cry, petition, prayer

8. **principle**
   (prin' sə pəl)

   (n.) a basic rule or law on which others are based; a belief used to tell right from wrong

   A judge must be a person of high _____ principles _____.

   SYNONYMS: a standard, truth, guide, guideline, creed

9. **realistic**
   (rē ə lis' tik)

   (adj.) using facts and good sense to evaluate people, things, or situations; concerned with the practical; resembling real life

   The painting was so _____ realistic _____ that it looked like a photograph.

   SYNONYMS: achievable, reasonable, sensible; true-to-life
   ANTONYMS: impractical, dreamy, unrealistic, pie-in-the-sky

10. **security**
    (si kyür' ə tē)

    (n.) freedom from danger, fear, or doubt; safety

    There is always heavy _____ security _____ around the White House.

    SYNONYMS: protection, safekeeping, confidence, assurance
    ANTONYMS: doubt, insecurity, peril

11. **selective**
    (sə lek' tiv)

    (adj.) very careful about choosing or using

    It pays to be a very _____ selective _____ shopper.

    SYNONYMS: choosy, particular, picky, fussy, discriminating
    ANTONYMS: unselective, careless

12. **tart**
    (tärt)

    (adj.) having a sharp or sour taste; sharp in manner or tone

    My sister replied with a very _____ tart _____ remark.

    (n.) a small pie, usually filled with fruit

    I had a peach _____ tart _____ for dessert.

    SYNONYMS: (adj.) tangy, acid; biting, cutting, harsh; (n.) a pastry
    ANTONYMS: (adj.) sweet; mild, gentle

97

For each item below, choose the word whose meaning is suggested by the clue given. Then write the word in the space provided.

1. To cuddle up with something is to _____ nestle _____.
   a. nestle   b. navigate   c. ensure   d. classify

2. If you make sure of something, you _____ ensure _____ it.
   a. nestle   b. ensure   c. classify   d. navigate

3. A person of high _____ principles _____ will always try to do good.
   a. avalanches   b. securities   c. pleas   d. principles

4. A fussy cat will be _____ selective _____ about what it eats.
   a. absurd   b. realistic   c. selective   d. tart

5. Freedom from fear leads to a sense of _____ security _____.
   a. principle   b. plea   c. avalanche   d. security

6. To decide how to label an item is to _____ classify _____ it.
   a. ensure   b. classify   c. navigate   d. nestle

7. An urgent appeal is a(n) _____ plea _____ for help.
   a. plea   b. security   c. avalanche   d. principle

8. Snow tumbling down a mountain is called a(n) _____ avalanche _____.
   a. plea   b. principle   c. avalanche   d. security

9. A statement that makes no sense is _____ absurd _____.
   a. realistic   b. absurd   c. selective   d. tart

10. If you judge a school on facts and evidence, you will probably get a(n)
    _____ realistic _____ sense of the place.
    a. absurd   b. selective   c. tart   d. realistic

11. To steer around obstacles is to _____ navigate _____ safely.
    a. ensure   b. navigate   c. classify   d. nestle

12. Lemonade without sugar tastes _____ tart _____.
    a. tart   b. selective   c. realistic   d. absurd

Synonyms

*For each item below, choose the word that is most nearly the **same** in meaning as the word or phrase in **boldface**. Then write your choice on the line provided.*

1. questioned our **standards**
   a. principles   b. securities   c. pleas   d. avalanches   _____ principles _____

2. a **landslide** of mail at holiday time
   a. plea   b. security   c. principle   d. avalanche   _____ avalanche _____

3. **appeals** to save the rain forest
   a. principles   b. avalanches   c. pleas   d. securities   _____ pleas _____

4. **sort** the blocks by shape and color
   a. navigate   b. ensure   c. nestle   d. classify   _____ classify _____

5. **cuddle** in my mother's arms
   a. classify   b. nestle   c. ensure   d. navigate   _____ nestle _____

6. **pilot** a tanker through the canal
   a. ensure   b. navigate   c. classify   d. nestle   _____ navigate _____

Antonyms

*For each item below, choose the word that is most nearly **opposite** in meaning to the word or phrase in **boldface**. Then write your choice on the line provided.*

1. to **deny** safe passage
   a. ensure   b. classify   c. navigate   d. nestle   _____ ensure _____

2. a **sound** excuse for being absent
   a. tart   b. absurd   c. realistic   d. selective   _____ absurd _____

3. show very **careless** taste
   a. selective   b. realistic   c. absurd   d. tart   _____ selective _____

4. an **impractical** view of the situation
   a. absurd   b. realistic   c. selective   d. tart   _____ realistic _____

5. prefer **sweet** apples
   a. selective   b. realistic   c. tart   d. absurd   _____ tart _____

6. felt a sense of **danger**
   a. avalanche   b. security   c. plea   d. principle   _____ security _____

Completing the Sentence

From the list of words on pages 96–97, choose the one that best completes each item below. Then write the word in the space provided. (You may have to change the word's ending.)

■ Some dogs are grouped by breed or by the work that they do. Collies and komondors, for example, are labeled as herding dogs because they are both used to protect and herd sheep. Highly trained dogs that work to help people are _____ classified _____ as assistance dogs.

■ Handlers of these animals have to be very _____ selective _____ in choosing dogs for the demanding training. Some animals are simply not suited to the work.

■ Some dogs, such as police or guard dogs, offer _____ security _____ from crime or trespassers, helping their owners feel safer in their homes. German shepherds and Doberman pinschers are among the best known of these breeds.

■ Rescue dogs can go where humans can not or dare not go. For example, these dogs can safely _____ navigate _____ the ruins or rubble left by earthquakes or accidents, in search of survivors.

■ Large, strong dogs with thick fur, such as St. Bernards or huskies, are trained to rescue skiers or climbers trapped by _____ avalanches _____.

■ Schools for these remarkable dogs make yearly _____ pleas _____ for money and for volunteers who will help prepare puppies for "canine careers."

CLOWNING AROUND

■ Like other schools, the Ringling Brothers Clown College is guided by a philosophy of education. At the Clown College, the first and foremost _____ principle _____ is that just about anyone can be taught the art of clowning.

■ To _____ ensure _____ success as clowns, students must work hard to master many skills, including juggling, acrobatics, makeup design, and comedy writing.

■ Great clowns make sensible, ordinary tasks, like opening a box, somehow seem _____ absurd _____ and wacky.

■ Sarcastic clowns use insults and _____ tart _____ comments to get laughs. Occasionally they make fun of people in the audience, but usually the clowns themselves are the butts of their own jokes.

■ In one funny routine, a clown dressed as a porcupine _____ nestled _____ against a cactus and called it "Mama."

■ The cactus looked quite _____ realistic _____ and lifelike from a distance, but on closer inspection it proved to be made of rubber.

Word Associations

*Circle the letter next to the word or expression that best completes the sentence or answers the question. Pay special attention to the word in **boldface**.*

1. Which would be an **absurd** gift for a two-year-old?
   a. a toy drum
   b. a beach ball
   c. a dinosaur puppet
   d. a real sports car

2. Where might you see an **avalanche**?
   a. on the ocean
   b. in the mountains
   c. in a desert
   d. in a suburb

3. You *cannot* be **classified** as
   a. a mammal
   b. a student
   c. a human being
   d. a plant

4. Which is a **plea**?
   a. "Thank you!"
   b. "That's an order!"
   c. "I forgot my lunch."
   d. "Not guilty, your honor."

5. Athletes with strong **principles**
   a. play by the rules
   b. fight with the coach
   c. hold out for more money
   d. skip practice

6. Studying hard will help **ensure**
   a. good manners
   b. good looks
   c. good weather
   d. good grades

7. Which will probably be **tart**?
   a. honey
   b. butterscotch pudding
   c. lemon juice
   d. blueberry pie

8. If a kitten **nestles**
   a. it scratches and howls
   b. it cuddles and purrs
   c. it chases a mouse
   d. it laps up milk

9. A movie about a **realistic** situation might be titled
   a. "I Married an Alligator!"
   b. "The Magic Eggplant"
   c. "Forest Fire!"
   d. "Martian Dance Party"

10. A sense of **security** makes you feel
    a. upset
    b. nervous
    c. safe
    d. lucky

11. A **selective** person might be called
    a. "Pokey Polly"
    b. "Picky Peter"
    c. "Wacky William"
    d. "Forgetful Fran"

12. Which is easiest to **navigate**?
    a. a bicycle
    b. a hot air balloon
    c. a bucking bronco
    d. a sailboat

Definitions

Study the spelling, pronunciation, part of speech, and definition given for each of the words below. Write the word in the blank space in the sentence that follows. Then read the synonyms and antonyms.

1. **abuse**
(*n.*, ə byüs′;
v., ə byüz′)

(n.) improper, wrong, or cruel treatment; insulting language
The _____abuse_____ of power is a danger in any government.

(v.) to put to bad use; to hurt or damage by treating badly
If you _____abuse_____ your privileges, they may be taken away.

SYNONYMS: (n.) misuse, mistreatment; (v.) to harm, injure; to insult
ANTONYMS: (n.) care, support; (v.) to cherish, honor, praise

2. **appliance**
(ə plī′ əns)

(n.) a machine or tool used to do a household job
It seemed an awfully big claim for such a little _____appliance_____.

SYNONYMS: a device, utensil, contraption, gadget

3. **confirm**
(kən fûrm′)

(v.) to agree or prove that something is true; to make sure, remove any doubt
The press secretary refused to _____confirm_____ the report.

SYNONYMS: to verify, support, assure; to check
ANTONYMS: to deny, disprove; to cancel

4. **daze**
(dāz)

(v.) to stun or confuse
Some predators _____daze_____ their prey with a blow to the head.

(n.) a state of confusion
When I heard that I had won the prize, I walked around in a _____daze_____.

SYNONYMS: (v.) to numb, shock, astound, baffle, bewilder; (n.) a trance, stupor

5. **flimsy**
(flim′ zē)

(adj.) not strong or solid; poorly made; not convincing
I don't think my teacher believed my _____flimsy_____ excuse for not doing my homework.

SYNONYMS: thin, light, weak, rickety, feeble; shabby, shoddy
ANTONYMS: strong, sturdy, sound; convincing

6. **gauge**
(gāj)

(n.) a standard measure used to tell size, thickness, and so on; an instrument used to measure
Weather scientists use a _____gauge_____ to measure rainfall.

(v.) to measure; to estimate
The cat seemed to _____gauge_____ the distance before jumping onto the windowsill.

SYNONYMS: (n.) a scale, rule, yardstick; (v.) to judge, assess; to guess

Ballerinas are taught to **rotate** (word 11)
while balancing on one toe in order
to perform pirouettes, or spins.

7. **migrant**
   (mi′ grənt)

   (n.) an animal or person that moves from one region to another as
   the seasons change; a farmworker who moves seasonally to pick
   different crops

   We passed a field full of _____migrants_____ *picking berries.*

   SYNONYMS: a traveler, nomad, drifter

8. **neutral**
   (nü′ trəl)

   (adj.) not taking any side in a disagreement or war; in-between,
   lacking distinction; not in gear

   Switzerland remained _____neutral_____ *through both World
   Wars I and II.*

   SYNONYMS: uninvolved, uncommitted, impartial, open-minded; indefinite, vague
   ANTONYMS: involved, committed, opinionated, heated; bold

9. **pitiless**
   (pi′ ti ləs)

   (adj.) showing no sorrow or regret for another's suffering or troubles

   The audience booed the _____pitiless_____ *villain.*

   SYNONYMS: cold, merciless, heartless, unsparing, cruel
   ANTONYMS: kindhearted, merciful, sympathetic

10. **presentable**
    (pri zen′ tə bəl)

    (adj.) fit to be seen or inspected

    My parents insisted that I wear _____presentable_____ *clothing.*

    SYNONYMS: suitable, proper, respectable, passable
    ANTONYMS: shabby, improper, unfit, unacceptable

11. **rotate**
    (ro′ tat)

    (v.) to turn around a central point; to alternate

    Do you know how long it takes Earth to _____rotate_____ *once?*

    SYNONYMS: to circle, twirl, spin; to change, switch

12. **shred**
    (shred)

    (n.) a thin strip; a tiny piece or amount

    Not a _____shred_____ *of evidence was found.*

    (v.) to cut or tear into thin strips or small pieces; to rip up

    The secretary was asked to _____shred_____ *the document.*

    SYNONYMS: (n.) a scrap, tatter, bit, fragment
    ANTONYMS: (n.) a whole; (v.) to fix, mend, repair

103

Match the Meaning

For each item below, choose the word whose meaning is suggested by the clue given. Then write the word in the space provided.

1. To use something in a way that brings harm to yourself or others is to _____abuse_____ it.
   a. gauge   b. rotate   c. daze   d. abuse

2. If you have been stunned, you might be in a(n) _____daze_____.
   a. gauge   b. daze   c. appliance   d. shred

3. To tear something to pieces is to _____shred_____ it.
   a. abuse   b. daze   c. shred   d. rotate

4. A _____pitiless_____ foe would not show mercy.
   a. flimsy   b. presentable   c. pitiless   d. neutral

5. Not to take sides is to remain _____neutral_____.
   a. pitiless   b. presentable   c. flimsy   d. neutral

6. To prove something is to _____confirm_____ it.
   a. daze   b. confirm   c. rotate   d. gauge

7. People or animals that move to different regions as the seasons change are called _____migrants_____.
   a. migrants   b. gauges   c. appliances   d. shreds

8. Blenders and can openers are kitchen _____appliances_____.
   a. migrants   b. shreds   c. appliances   d. gauges

9. Something poorly made is said to be _____flimsy_____.
   a. presentable   b. flimsy   c. pitiless   d. neutral

10. A room fit to be inspected is _____presentable_____.
    a. flimsy   b. pitiless   c. neutral   d. presentable

11. To alternate chores is to _____rotate_____ them.
    a. shred   b. rotate   c. abuse   d. gauge

12. You would use a _____gauge_____ to measure something.
    a. gauge   b. shred   c. daze   d. migrant

Synonyms

For each item below, choose the word that is most nearly the **same** in meaning as the word or phrase in **boldface**. Then write your choice on the line provided.

1. an electrical **device** for cleaning rugs
   a. shred   b. migrant   c. gauge   d. appliance   _____appliance_____

2. left behind by the **drifters**
   a. shreds   b. abuses   c. migrants   d. gauges   _____migrants_____

3. wore a **respectable** outfit for the class picture
   a. presentable b. flimsy   c. neutral   d. pitiless   _____presentable_____

4. **numbed** by the terrible news
   a. gauged   b. dazed   c. rotated   d. confirmed   _____dazed_____

5. **assess** the value of the coin collection
   a. shred   b. gauge   c. abuse   d. rotate   _____gauge_____

6. **twirl** the plant to face the sun
   a. confirm   b. gauge   c. daze   d. rotate   _____rotate_____

Antonyms

For each item below, choose the word that is most nearly **opposite** in meaning to the word or phrase in **boldface**. Then write your choice on the line provided.

1. **mend** the old pillowcase
   a. shred   b. confirm   c. rotate   d. gauge   _____shred_____

2. **sturdy** shoes
   a. neutral   b. flimsy   c. presentable d. pitiless   _____flimsy_____

3. reported their **kindhearted** treatment
   a. neutral   b. flimsy   c. presentable d. pitiless   _____pitiless_____

4. refused to **deny** the rumor
   a. gauge   b. rotate   c. confirm   d. classify   _____confirm_____

5. painted in **bold** colors
   a. flimsy   b. neutral   c. presentable d. pitiless   _____neutral_____

6. fans who **praise** the umpires
   a. rotate   b. gauge   c. abuse   d. daze   _____abuse_____

Completing the Sentence

From the list of words on pages 102–103, choose the one that best completes each item below. Then write the word in the space provided. (You may have to change the word's ending.)

A TOAST TO TOAST

■ One of the most common of household _____appliances_____, the electric toaster, was first introduced to American kitchens in 1910.

■ Early models toasted only one side of the bread at a time. In order to toast both sides, you had to _____rotate_____ the slice of bread yourself.

■ These toasters did not have self-timers, either. If you didn't pay careful attention, your toast might not look very _____presentable_____. And if it had turned to ashes, it might not even be fit to eat!

FROM FIELD TO FIELD

■ It is estimated that in the United States there are today about half a million _____migrants_____ who follow the harvest each year in search of work at fruit and vegetable farms.

■ Unfortunately, these workers are often _____abused_____ by harsh bosses who pay too little and demand too much. To make matters worse, working and living conditions are often unsafe and unsanitary.

■ Bending over for hours under a hot sun to harvest crops can leave these workers feeling _____dazed_____ by the end of a long day in the fields.

■ The _____pitiless_____ sun beats down on the workers, offering no mercy to man, woman, or child.

■ Some farmworkers are so poor that they barely get enough to eat, and their old, tattered clothes hang in _____shreds_____.

■ Rather than stay _____neutral_____ about the problems that seasonal farmworkers face, some activists are taking up their cause by fighting for improved legal and civil rights.

RUNNING ON EMPTY

■ When our car came sputtering to a stop on a dark and lonely country road, I was almost afraid to look at the fuel _____gauge_____.

■ But when I did, a quick glance was enough to _____confirm_____ the worst: The car had run out of gas, just as I suspected.

■ We had to walk two miles to a gas station, with nothing more to protect us from the rain than our _____flimsy_____ jackets. When we got back to the car with a container of fuel, we were completely soaked and shivering with cold.

*Circle the letter next to the word or expression that best completes the sentence or answers the question. Pay special attention to the word in **boldface.***

1. A **flimsy** toy will probably
   a. cost lots of money
   b. break much too soon
   c. be very popular
   d. come in many colors

2. To **confirm** a fact for a social studies report, you might
   a. check an encyclopedia
   b. read a science-fiction novel
   c. copy the paper neatly
   d. call your doctor

3. If you're in a **daze**, you may
   a. yell at your friends
   b. remember to water the plants
   c. not notice the time
   d. turn the calendar page

4. Birds that are **migrants** probably
   a. have blue feathers
   b. lay only one egg at a time
   c. eat fruits and vegetables
   d. travel in the spring and fall

5. Which is known for **rotating**?
   a. a teddy bear
   b. a top
   c. a book
   d. a sandwich

6. A **neutral** nation would not be
   a in debt
   b. an island
   c. at war
   d. at peace

7. Which is easiest to **shred**?
   a. a loaf of bread
   b. a brass ring
   c. a suit of armor
   d. a spike

8. A piano that has been **abused**
   a. would sound better
   b. might be out of tune
   c. would increase in value
   d. might be hard to move

9. A **pitiless** person would make others
   a. feel unloved
   b. feel unfamiliar
   c. feel at ease
   d. feel proud

10. Which might you need to **gauge**?
    a. the distance from Earth to the moon
    b. a friend's height
    c. the amount of gold in Fort Knox
    d. the width of a cat's whisker

11. To make your room more **presentable**, you might
    a. feed your hamster
    b. put away your clothes and toys
    c. open the window
    d. lock the door

12. Which is an **appliance**?
    a. a box of laundry detergent
    b. a laundry room
    c. a laundry basket
    d. a washing machine

REVIEW UNITS 9–12

Internet

For vocabulary games and activities,
visit **www.sadlier-oxford.com**.

Selecting Word Meanings

*For each of the following items, circle the choice that is
most nearly the **same** in meaning as the word in **boldface**.*

1. check the latest opinion **poll**
   a. speech   **b. survey**   c. software   d. timetable

2. learn **thrifty** habits
   a. money-saving   b. childish   c. wasteful   d. nervous

3. **rotate** the schedule
   a. write   b. memorize   **c. switch**   d. stick to

4. **identical** patterns
   a. matching   b. complicated   c. unusual   d. colorful

5. **neutral** reporting
   a. opinionated   b. careless   c. realistic   **d. unbiased**

6. **classify** the types of insects
   a. read about   b. preserve   **c. catalog**   d. photograph

7. **humiliated** the defending champions
   a. congratulated   **b. embarrassed**   c. cheered for   d. disliked

8. **confirm** the dental appointment
   a. make sure of   b. reschedule   c. cancel   d. fear

9. studied the **principles** of multiplication
   a. questions   b. challenges   **c. rules**   d. theories

10. a **brisk** early morning swim
    a. slow   b. relaxing   c. exhausting   **d. energetic**

11. **expand** the search
    a. join   **b. widen**   c. end   d. begin

12. **considerate** neighbors
    a. friendly   b. noisy   **c. thoughtful**   d. sneaky

Spelling

For each item below, study the **boldface** word in which there is a blank. If a letter is missing, fill in the blank to make a correctly spelled word. If the word is already spelled correctly, leave the blank empty.

1. numbers on a **ga__uge**
2. an **avalanch e of bills**
3. **so o the** my aching head
4. a desperate **ple__a**
5. a labor-saving **ap p liance**
6. lost in a **da__ze**

7. **condem n** the attack
8. **des c end** a staircase
9. **migr a nt** whales
10. an **abs u rd** suggestion
11. a **present a ble** appearance
12. fought against the **dictat o r**

Antonyms

For each of the following items, circle the choice that is most nearly the **opposite** in meaning to the word in **boldface** in the introductory phrase.

1. **confirmed** my fears
   a. explained   (b.) disproved   c. ignored   d. supported

2. **brittle** tree branches
   a. stiff   b. slender   (c.) bendable   d. thick

3. **shred** the old photograph
   (a.) mend   b. tear up   c. throw away   d. lose

4. **tart** fruits
   a. tangy   b. ripe   c. frozen   (d.) sweet

5. speak out against **abuse**
   (a.) kindness   b. mistreatment   c. knowledge   d. humor

6. a **portable** stage
   (a.) fixed   b. movable   c. small   d. bare

7. a **flimsy** explanation
   a. lengthy   b. weak   c. complicated   (d.) convincing

8. **improper** way of doing things
   a. wrong   b. awkward   (c.) correct   d. simple

Vocabulary for Comprehension

*Read the following passage in which some of the words you have studied appear in **boldface**. Then answer the questions on page 111.*

Making Sense of a Scientific Survey

The U.S. Census Bureau takes official surveys to gather data on our population. The formal count is called a *census*. Business leaders, educators, and politicians use the data to get a **realistic** picture of the people they serve and the needs of the community.

Scientists also use census data. Can you imagine why? Scientists study plant and animal populations for many reasons. Scientists might track animal populations to learn how animals and humans can live together safely. They might study specific fish populations in a pond to get information about water pollution. Or they might count the members of an endangered species to **confirm** that the animals need ongoing protection.

Government census workers gather data in person and by mail. But scientists must find unique ways to count the plants or animals in a given area. To **estimate** the population of free-tailed bats in Carlsbad Cavern, the largest cave in New Mexico, scientists made use of technology. They set up video cameras outside the entrance of the cave, which houses a large number of bats. The scientists taped the bats flying out of the cave. Later, they counted the bats in each frame of the video.

Free-tailed bats emerging from caves to hunt

Scientists sometimes use just their eyes to take a census. This **visual** method works best when the plants or animals are large in size and small in number. For example, to count the maple trees on a farm in Vermont, scientists can simply use their eyes. A more complex method would be needed to determine the number of small animals, such as field mice, in the same **vicinity**.

Fill in the circle next to the choice that best completes the sentence
or answers the question.

1. What is the main idea of this article?
   (a) The U.S. Census Bureau gathers useful population data.
   (b) Like the government, scientists gather and use census data.
   (c) Carlsbad, New Mexico, is an interesting place to visit.
   (d) Scientists use their eyes to count many living things.

2. The meaning of **realistic** is
   (a) true-to-life
   (b) scientific
   (c) superb
   (d) strict

3. Another word for **confirm** is
   (a) question
   (b) disprove
   (c) suggest
   (d) verify

4. Scientists might investigate plant and animal populations
   (a) to learn about polluted cities
   (b) to educate American voters
   (c) to see if a species is endangered
   (d) to test new voting machines

5. In this passage, **estimate** means
   (a) calculation
   (b) opinion
   (c) figure
   (d) praise

6. The method for counting bats described in this passage involves
   (a) using just eyes
   (b) gathering data by mail
   (c) questioning neighbors
   (d) videotaping a cave entrance

7. **Visual** means having to do with
   (a) sound or hearing
   (b) sight or seeing
   (c) feel or touching
   (d) scent or smelling

8. Another word for **vicinity** is
   (a) tally
   (b) state
   (c) area
   (d) laboratory

9. This article was written to inform people of
   (a) how scientists gather and use data
   (b) an estimation technique
   (c) the need for scientific data
   (d) a new plant species

10. Which is the most likely topic for the next paragraph in the article?
   (a) when the first census was taken
   (b) the number of farms in Vermont
   (c) the way to take a census of small forest animals
   (d) other wildlife in Carlsbad

Grammar in Context

An **adjective** is a word that describes a noun. It tells what the person, place, or thing is like.

Use the correct form of an adjective when you compare.

You usually add **er** to an adjective to compare two or more people, places, or things.

Ice Cave is **larger** than Lava Cave.

You usually add **est** to an adjective to compare three or more people, places, or things.

Carlsbad Caverns is the **largest** cave in New Mexico.

*For adjectives ending in **e**, drop the **e** before adding **er** or **est**.*

*Use the correct form of the adjective in **boldface** to complete the sentence. Then write the sentence on the line.*

1. A healthy branch is (**strong**) than a dry and brittle twig. _A healthy branch is_ _stronger than a dry and brittle twig._

2. The bats prey upon the (**small**) insects of all. _The bats prey upon the smallest_ _insects of all._

3. Bats can navigate even on the (**dark**) nights. _Bats can navigate even on the darkest_ _nights._

4. The visitors descend into the (**deep**) cave in New Mexico. _The visitors descend into_ _the deepest cave in New Mexico._

5. The security guard directs us to the (**close**) exit. _The security guard directs us to the_ _closest exit._

6. The guard's jacket is (**warm**) than my flimsy sweater. _The guard's jacket is warmer_ _than my flimsy sweater._

 **Completing the Idea**

*Complete each sentence so that it makes sense. Pay attention to the word in **boldface**.*

Accept answers that show an understanding of the vocabulary.

1. I take **brisk** walks in the morning because _____.

2. The twins are nearly **identical**, except that _____.

3. In a **poll** about the election, I was asked _____.

4. A good way to **soothe** sore feet is to _____.

5. A folding table is **portable** because _____.

6. We could **expand** the team by _____.

7. Because of the **famine**, many people _____.

8. To **ensure** that I wake up on time, I will _____.

9. I like to **classify** my books by _____.

10. If I **shred** the pages in my diary, then _____.

11. I have a sense of **security** knowing that _____.

12. For a **tart** taste, I recommend _____.

13. One household **appliance** I cannot live without is _____.

14. I was in a **daze** when I heard that _____.

15. To look more **presentable**, please _____.

Write Your Own

Choose a word from Units 9–12. Write a sentence using the word. If your sentence contains an adjective, be sure you used the correct form of the adjective.

Check that the vocabulary is used correctly and that the sentence is written correctly.

_____

Word Families

*The words in **boldface** in the sentences below are related to words introduced in Units 9–12. For example, the nouns* confirmation *and* navigation *in item 1 are related to the verbs* confirm *(Unit 12) and* navigate *(Unit 11). Based on your understanding of the unit words that follow, circle the related word in **boldface** that best completes each sentence.*

absurd	abuse	classify	condemn	confirm
considerate	descend	displace	estimate	expand
flimsy	humiliate	improper	migrant	navigate
neutral	poll	portable	presentable	rotate

1. The U.S. Senate is responsible for the (**confirmation**/**navigation**) of the President's nominees for ambassadorships.

2. Queen Elizabeth II of England is a direct (**classification**/**descendant**) of Queen Victoria.

3. A figure skater who successfully performs a quadruple jump completes four (**rotations**/**considerations**) in the air.

4. A public official who takes a bribe is guilty of (**impropriety**/**absurdity**).

5. Scientists use photographs of the one-of-a-kind markings on the tail fins of humpback whales as one tool in tracking the (**migration**/**expansion**) of these marine mammals.

6. During an election campaign, (**pollsters**/**abusers**) question voters about which candidates they prefer.

7. One of the advantages of a personal stereo is its (**presentability**/**portability**).

8. In math we learn that (**displacement**/**estimation**) can sometimes help us solve problems.

9. While a trial is in progress, the judge repeatedly instructs the jury to maintain its (**neutrality**/**flimsiness**) until all the testimony and evidence have been presented.

10. The politician's insensitive remarks received public (**humiliation**/**condemnation**).

Use the clues below to complete the crossword puzzle.
(All of the answers are words from Units 9–12.)

```
 1                              2          3
 D                             V I C I N I T Y
 I                                         A
 4                                         R
 S H R E D                 5       6
 P                         R E A L I S T I C
 L                             B
 7              8           9          10
 F A M I N E               D O W N F A L L
 C          E                 L      L
 E          S                 I      I
        11                            
        P I T I L E S S        M
           L                   I
        12                  S   S
        P R E Y                 H   Y
```

Down

1. to move aside
3.
6. do away with completely
8. cuddle
10. poorly made

Across

2. neighborhood
4. tear to bits
5. lifelike
7. widespread hunger
9. collapse or ruin
11. without mercy
12. predator's victim

Definitions

Study the spelling, pronunciation, part of speech, and definition given for each of the words below. Write the word in the blank space in the sentence that follows. Then read the synonyms and antonyms.

1. **achievement**
(ə chēv′ mənt)

(n.) something done successfully; something gained by working or trying hard
A perfect report card is quite an _____achievement_____.
SYNONYMS: an accomplishment, feat, triumph
ANTONYMS: a defeat, failure, setback

2. **acquire**
(ə kwīr′)

(v.) to get as one's own
When did you _____acquire_____ *the ability to speak French so well?*
SYNONYMS: to obtain, gain, earn
ANTONYMS: to lose, give up, surrender

3. **debate**
(di bāt′)

(n.) a discussion of reasons for and against something
The town council held a _____debate_____ *on building a new library.*
(v.) to discuss reasons for and against something; to think about carefully before deciding
What issue would you like to _____debate_____?
SYNONYMS: (n.) an argument, dispute; (v.) to discuss, consider
ANTONYMS: (n.) an agreement; (v.) to agree (with)

4. **exhibit**
(ig zi′ bət)

(v.) to show clearly; to put on display
You _____exhibit_____ *great talent in gymnastics.*
(n.) something shown to the public
We went to the diamond _____exhibit_____ *at the science museum.*
SYNONYMS: (v.) to present, reveal; (n.) a display, exhibition
ANTONYMS: (v.) to hide, conceal, cover up

5. **foe**
(fō)

(n.) one who hates or tries to harm another; an enemy
Identify yourself: Are you friend or _____foe_____?
SYNONYMS: an opponent, rival
ANTONYMS: a friend, ally, comrade, buddy

6. **latter**
(la′ tər)

(adj.) closer to the end; relating to the second of two things discussed
The first part of the movie is good, but the _____latter_____ *part drags on too long.*
SYNONYMS: last, later, end, final
ANTONYMS: former, first, earlier, beginning

Some people who make computer parts have to wear special clothing to keep their work area completely **sanitary** (word 10).

7. **massacre**
(ma′ si kər)

(n.) the cruel killing of many people or animals
The village was the site of a bloody _____massacre_____.

(v.) to kill many people or animals in a cruel way
The barbarians planned to _____massacre_____ their rivals.

SYNONYMS: (n.) a slaughter; (v.) to butcher, slaughter

8. **monotonous**
(mə nä′ tən əs)

(adj.) dull as a result of not changing in any way
Shelling peas is a _____monotonous_____ chore.

SYNONYMS: boring, uninteresting, tiresome
ANTONYMS: varied, lively, exciting

9. **preserve**
(pri zûrv′)

(v.) to keep safe from injury or ruin; to keep food from spoiling
I signed a petition to _____preserve_____ the wetlands.

(n.) an area set aside for the protection of wildlife
Wild animals roam freely in the nature _____preserve_____.

SYNONYMS: (v.) to save, protect, conserve; (n.) a refuge, sanctuary
ANTONYMS: (v.) to waste, destroy, misuse

10. **sanitary**
(sa′ nə ter ē)

(adj.) having to do with health; free of dirt and germs
A health inspector checks _____sanitary_____ conditions in a restaurant.

SYNONYMS: clean, pure, sterile, hygienic
ANTONYMS: dirty, filthy, contaminated, unhealthy

11. **sprawl**
(sprôl)

(v.) to lie or sit with arms and legs spread out; to spread out in a disorderly way
Some nights I _____sprawl_____ in front of the TV set.

SYNONYMS: to lounge, slouch, relax, stretch, extend

12. **widespread**
(wīd′ spred′)

(adj.) happening in many places or to many people; fully open
Interest in the lives of movie stars is _____widespread_____.

SYNONYMS: far-reaching, vast, common
ANTONYMS: limited, rare, unusual, uncommon

117

Match the Meaning

For each item below, choose the word whose meaning is suggested by the clue given. Then write the word in the space provided.

1. A display of paintings or other objects is a(n) _____exhibit_____.
   a. debate   b. exhibit   c. massacre   d. preserve

2. A belief that is held by many people is _____widespread_____.
   a. latter   b. monotonous   c. widespread   d. sanitary

3. When you buy property, you _____acquire_____ it.
   a. massacre   b. sprawl   c. debate   d. acquire

4. People who hate one another are _____foes_____.
   a. achievements   b. foes   c. debates   d. exhibits

5. The cruel killing of many innocent people is a(n) _____massacre_____.
   a. massacre   b. exhibit   c. achievement   d. foe

6. Something that is free of germs is _____sanitary_____.
   a. widespread   b. monotonous   c. latter   d. sanitary

7. To consider the pros and cons of an issue is to _____debate_____ it.
   a. debate   b. exhibit   c. preserve   d. acquire

8. A bird sanctuary is an example of a wildlife _____preserve_____.
   a. debate   b. massacre   c. preserve   d. foe

9. The second of two events is the _____latter_____ one.
   a. monotonous   b. latter   c. sanitary   d. widespread

10. Landing on the moon is an example of a(n) _____achievement_____.
    a. foe   b. achievement   c. massacre   d. preserve

11. Something that is done over and over in the same way is _____monotonous_____.
    a. latter   b. widespread   c. sanitary   d. monotonous

12. To lie on the floor with your arms and legs spread out is to _____sprawl_____.
    a. exhibit   b. preserve   c. sprawl   d. acquire

Synonyms

*For each item below, choose the word that is most nearly the **same** in meaning as the word or phrase in **boldface**. Then write your choice on the line provided.*

1. a worthy **opponent**
   a. preserve   b. exhibit   c. foe   d. debate   _____ foe _____

2. **slaughter** the newborn harp seals
   a. preserve   b. exhibit   c. acquire   d. massacre   _____ massacre _____

3. the **boring** refrain of "tra-la-la"
   a. latter   b. sanitary   c. widespread   d. monotonous   _____ monotonous _____

4. **consider** going by train or by car
   a. sprawl   b. debate   c. acquire   d. massacre   _____ debate _____

5. my proudest **accomplishment**
   a. preserve   b. exhibit   c. foe   d. achievement   _____ achievement _____

6. **lounge** on the couch
   a. exhibit   b. preserve   c. sprawl   d. massacre   _____ sprawl _____

Antonyms

*For each item below, choose the word that is most nearly **opposite** in meaning to the word or phrase in **boldface**. Then write your choice on the line provided.*

1. **conceal** your surprise
   a. exhibit   b. sprawl   c. massacre   d. preserve   _____ exhibit _____

2. the **first** part of our vacation
   a. widespread   b. latter   c. monotonous   d. sanitary   _____ latter _____

3. **lose** millions of dollars
   a. debate   b. sprawl   c. massacre   d. acquire   _____ acquire _____

4. **limited** appeal among children
   a. sanitary   b. monotonous   c. latter   d. widespread   _____ widespread _____

5. **destroy** the town records
   a. massacre   b. exhibit   c. preserve   d. sprawl   _____ preserve _____

6. found **unhealthy** living conditions
   a. latter   b. sanitary   c. widespread   d. monotonous   _____ sanitary _____

Completing the Sentence

From the list of words on pages 116–117, choose the one that best completes each item below. Write the word in the space provided. (You may have to change the word's ending.)

■ The current events club had to decide whether to _____**debate**_____ hunters' rights or the child helmet law.

■ We chose the child helmet law, the _____**latter**_____ issue, because it was more relevant to students our age.

■ The members of our team gave such _____**monotonous**_____ speeches in favor of the law that the other team won, although their arguments were more emotional than fact-filled.

WHAT HAPPENED IN RWANDA

■ In 1994 a brutal _____**massacre**_____ took place in Rwanda, a country in Central Africa. Hundreds of thousands of people were injured or killed.

■ The major _____**foes**_____ were the Hutu and Tutsi peoples.

■ In overcrowded refugee camps, _____**sanitary**_____ conditions were dangerously poor. Clean water, food, and medicines were in short supply.

■ Rescue workers found entire families _____**sprawled**_____ on the ground. Many of these people were dying of starvation and disease.

"FOUR SCORE AND SEVEN YEARS AGO. . ."

■ Many historians consider Abraham Lincoln's Gettysburg Address to be the greatest _____**achievement**_____ in public speaking this nation has produced.

■ The fame of this brief speech is so _____**widespread**_____ that most Americans—and even many from other nations—know the opening of it by heart.

■ The Library of Congress _____**acquired**_____ a copy of the speech, written in Lincoln's own hand. Only four other copies in his handwriting are still in existence.

■ At the library the manuscript is carefully _____**preserved**_____ as a national historical treasure.

■ Sometimes the document travels to Pennsylvania for _____**exhibit**_____ in connection with special events at the actual site of the battle. The battlefield became a national park in 1895.

Word Associations

*Circle the letter next to the word or expression that best completes the sentence or answers the question. Pay special attention to the word in **boldface.***

1. A cafeteria that is **sanitary** has
   a. good main dishes
   b. overflowing trash bins
   c. safely prepared food
   d. high-priced lunches

2. The **latter** part of December includes
   a. the first day of the month
   b. the last week of the month
   c. four Sundays
   d. New Year's Day

3. If my neighbor is my **foe,** we
   a. share a driveway
   b. do not get along
   c. live in the country
   d. feed each other's pets

4. Witnesses to a **massacre** probably feel
   a. horrified
   b. cheerful
   c. hungry
   d. relaxed

5. A **monotonous** speaker might
   a. win an award for public speaking
   b. wake up the neighborhood
   c. give speech lessons
   d. put a listener to sleep

6. A swimmer who is honored for his or her **achievements** might
   a. go waterskiing
   b. get a sunburn
   c. get a trophy
   d. go to an aquarium

7. Which of these has been **preserved**?
   a. apples on a tree
   b. berries on a vine
   c. fresh peach pie
   d. canned pears

8. Which might be included in an **exhibit** of students' work?
   a. paintings by famous artists
   b. science fair projects
   c. parents and teachers
   d. rulers and erasers

9. One way to **acquire** a rare stamp is to
   a. mail a letter
   b. read a book about collecting stamps
   c. buy one from a catalog
   d. pay extra postage

10. A participant in a **debate** should
    a. defend his or her point of view
    b. try not to say anything
    c. never argue with an opponent
    d. join the football team

11. Which of these is **widespread**?
    a. an opinion held by a few friends
    b. a belief that the earth is flat
    c. an interest in fruitflies
    d. a disease that infects many people

12. I might **sprawl** on the couch to
    a. relax
    b. wake up
    c. move furniture
    d. exercise

Definitions

Study the spelling, pronunciation, part of speech, and definition given for each of the words below. Write the word in the blank space in the sentence that follows. Then read the synonyms and antonyms.

1. **alibi**
   (a' lə bī)

   (n.) a claim of having been elsewhere when a crime was committed; a reason given to explain something
   Can anyone confirm your _____alibi_____?
   SYNONYMS: an excuse, explanation, story, defense

2. **confederate**
   (kən fe' də rət)

   (adj.) joined with others for a common purpose
   Seven sheikdoms are _____confederate_____ states in the United Arab Emirates.

   (n.) a person, state, or country that joins with another for a common purpose; a partner in crime
   Some of our wartime allies are still our _____confederates_____ in peacekeeping organizations.
   SYNONYMS: (adj.) united, allied, combined; (n.) an ally, accomplice
   ANTONYMS: (adj.) divided, separated; (n.) a foe, enemy

3. **discharge**
   (*v.*, dis chärj';
   n., dis' chärj)

   (v.) to let go; to unload cargo or passengers; to fire off; to give off
   Did the hospital _____discharge_____ the patient?

   (n.) a release or letting go; a firing off; a giving off; something given off
   A search of the records showed that the army gave the soldier an honorable _____discharge_____.
   SYNONYMS: (v.) to release, dismiss, shoot; (n.) a dismissal
   ANTONYMS: (v.) to detain, imprison; to hire, appoint; to load; to absorb

4. **economical**
   (e kə nä' mi kəl)

   (adj.) careful about spending money or using resources
   An _____economical_____ shopper waits for sales and always looks for a bargain.
   SYNONYMS: thrifty, frugal, saving
   ANTONYMS: extravagant, wasteful

5. **frank**
   (fraŋk)

   (adj.) honest in expressing thoughts and feelings
   Don't be offended if I am _____frank_____ with you.
   SYNONYMS: direct, blunt, straightforward, truthful
   ANTONYMS: secretive, insincere, dishonest

6. **modify**
   (mä' də fī)

   (v.) to change somewhat
   A good cook knows how to _____modify_____ a recipe if one or two of the ingredients are not available.
   SYNONYMS: to adjust, alter, adapt, vary, revise

7. **mutiny**
(myü′ tən ē)

(n.) an open rebellion against authority
The Boston Tea Party was an act of _____mutiny_____.
(v.) to rebel against those in charge
The captain's cruelty led the crew to _____mutiny_____.
SYNONYMS: (n.) a revolt, uprising, riot; (v.) to revolt, rise up
ANTONYMS: (n.) to support, obey

8. **negative**
(ne′ gə tiv)

(adj.) saying "no"; not positive or helpful; less than zero; having the same electric charge as an electron
The reply to my question was ___negative___.
(n.) an expression that says "no"; a photographic image in which light and dark areas are reversed
"I can't" is an example of a _____negative_____.
SYNONYMS: (adj.) bad, unfavorable
ANTONYMS: (adj.) positive, helpful, good, favorable

9. **pursue**
(pər sü′)

(v.) to chase in order to catch; to strive to achieve; to carry out
During a hunt the dogs _____pursue_____ *a hare.*
SYNONYMS: to follow, hunt, run after, aim for, work for
ANTONYMS: to run away, take off, flee, bolt

10. **reign**
(rān)

(n.) the power or rule of a monarch; a monarch's period of rule
England prospered under the _____reign_____ *of Queen Anne.*
(v.) to rule as a monarch; to be widespread
During the 1920s, prosperity ___reigned___.
SYNONYMS: (n.) the regime, control; (v.) to govern, command

11. **singular**
(siŋ′ gyə lər)

(adj.) referring to one person or thing only; out of the ordinary
The show was a _____singular_____ *success.*
(n.) the form of a word that is used to refer to one person or thing
"Mouse" is the _____singular_____ *of "mice."*
SYNONYMS: (adj.) exceptional, unusual
ANTONYMS: (adj.) plural; (n.) a plural

12. **swindle**
(swin′ dəl)

(v.) to cheat out of money or property
A dishonest shopkeeper tried to _____swindle_____ *me.*
(n.) a scheme for cheating someone
The fraud squad uncovered the _____swindle_____.
SYNONYMS: (v.) to deceive, trick, gyp, con; (n.) a scam, fraud, hoax, racket

Match the Meaning

For each item below, choose the word whose meaning is suggested by the clue given. Then write the word in the space provided.

1. To rebel against commanding officers is to _____ mutiny _____.
   a. discharge   b. swindle   c. modify   d. mutiny

2. To exercise the powers of a king or queen is to _____ reign _____.
   a. reign   b. pursue   c. mutiny   d. modify

3. A scheme for cheating people is a _____ swindle _____.
   a. negative   b. discharge   c. swindle   d. confederate

4. A claim of being elsewhere during a crime is a(n) _____ alibi _____.
   a. alibi   b. mutiny   c. discharge   d. reign

5. When you change plans slightly, you _____ modify _____ them.
   a. modify   b. discharge   c. swindle   d. pursue

6. A person who freely expresses his or her opinion is _____ frank _____.
   a. confederate   b. economical   c. negative   d. frank

7. When you fire a gun, you _____ discharge _____ it.
   a. swindle   b. discharge   c. pursue   d. modify

8. A person who is careful about spending money is _____ economical _____.
   a. frank   b. negative   c. economical   d. singular

9. A person who makes a suggestion that is not helpful is being _____ negative _____.
   a. economical   b. negative   c. frank   d. singular

10. A willing accomplice to a robbery is a(n) _____ confederate _____ of the thief.
    a. confederate   b. alibi   c. discharge   d. mutiny

11. The anniversary celebration was the _____ singular _____ event of the year.
    a. frank   b. singular   c. confederate   d. economical

12. When you keep trying to achieve a goal, you _____ pursue _____ it.
    a. modify   b. discharge   c. pursue   d. swindle

Synonyms

*For each item below, choose the word that is most nearly the **same** in meaning as the word or phrase in **boldface**. Then write your choice on the line provided.*

1. a **blunt** answer to your question
   a. frank   b. negative   c. singular   d. confederate   _____frank_____

2. **revise** the schedule
   a. discharge   b. pursue   c. modify   d. swindle   _____modify_____

3. **aim for** a career in medicine
   a. modify   b. discharge   c. swindle   d. pursue   _____pursue_____

4. an ironclad **excuse**
   a. confederate b. reign   c. alibi   d. mutiny   _____alibi_____

5. a **regime** of terror
   a. swindle   b. discharge   c. mutiny   d. reign   _____reign_____

6. **cheated** by a con artist
   a. pursued   b. swindled   c. modified   d. discharged   _____swindled_____

Antonyms

*For each item below, choose the word that is most nearly **opposite** in meaning to the word or phrase in **boldface**. Then write your choice on the line provided.*

1. **positive** numbers
   a. negative   b. singular   c. economical d. confederate   _____negative_____

2. the **wasteful** use of natural resources
   a. frank   b. economical c. singular   d. negative   _____economical_____

3. soldiers who **obey**
   a. discharge   b. mutiny   c. reign   d. swindle   _____mutiny_____

4. **load** a cannon
   a. modify   b. pursue   c. swindle   d. discharge   _____discharge_____

5. **plural** nouns
   a. negative   b. economical c. singular   d. frank   _____singular_____

6. **enemies** of the tribe
   a. reigns   b. alibis   c. mutinies   d. confederates   _____confederates_____

Completing the Sentence

From the list of words on pages 122–123, choose the one that best completes each item below. Write the word in the space provided. (You may have to change the word's ending.)

EDITING AN ESSAY

■ When I write an essay, I start with a rough draft. Then I review what I have written to see how I can improve it. One way that I may _____ modify _____ the essay is to get rid of any repetitions.

■ Because I want to keep the reader's attention, I try to keep my sentences clear and brief. Therefore, I look for more _____ economical _____ ways to make my points.

■ For example, if I am writing about two people, I may want to use the plural pronoun *they* instead of _____ singular _____ pronouns such as *he* and *she*. As a last step I reread the essay to make sure there are no errors of spelling, grammar, or punctuation.

TROUBLE ON THE HIGH SEAS

■ Captain William Bligh, an English admiral, _____ reigned _____ over his ship, the *Bounty,* as if he were its king.

■ His harsh treatment and mean-spirited rules aroused _____ negative _____ feelings among crew members. Few viewed the captain in a favorable light.

■ In a secret but _____ frank _____ discussion, the sailors plotted to take over the ship.

■ A ship's officer named Fletcher Christian seized control of the *Bounty* on April 28, 1789. This daring _____ mutiny _____ has been the subject of several popular movies.

CRIME AT THE CASH MACHINE

■ Soon after my uncle opened a checking account at a new bank, he was the victim of a bank machine _____ swindle _____.

■ A woman posing as a banker and her _____ confederate _____, who said he was the manager, advised my uncle to get $200 from the cash machine to test his bank card. The crooks then ran off with my uncle's money.

■ Using the descriptions given by my uncle and a witness, the police _____ pursued _____ the two thieves on foot, catching up to them a few blocks away.

■ They soon arrested the suspects without having to _____ discharge _____ their weapons.

■ At their trial the two thieves claimed that they were innocent. But the jury did not believe their _____ alibis _____. It took the jury only fifteen minutes to find them guilty.

*Circle the letter next to the word or expression that best completes the sentence or answers the question. Pay special attention to the word in **boldface**.*

1. A **frank** comment is
   a. always complimentary
   b. never hurtful
   c. always appreciated
   d. never dishonest

2. An **economical** car probably
   a. stalls frequently
   b. uses little gas
   c. pollutes the air
   d. runs on air

3. Infantry soldiers who **mutiny** are likely to
   a. get medals
   b. be promoted
   c. get new uniforms
   d. be punished

4. To **modify** a drawing you might
   a. erase a few lines
   b. crumple it up
   c. show it to a friend
   d. go to a museum

5. Which of these is a good **alibi**?
   a. "I didn't do it."
   b. "I was in school at that time."
   c. "I saw them rob the store."
   d. "I hope you catch the crook."

6. Which of these is a **singular** noun?
   a. chicks
   b. geese
   c. goose
   d. ducks

7. A **negative** person is likely to
   a. take great vacation pictures
   b. be good at math
   c. find fault with any plan
   d. see the best in everyone

8. A **reigning** king probably has
   a. boots and an umbrella
   b. a scepter and a crown
   c. a computer and a modem
   d. a bow and an arrow

9. If I **swindle** my little brother, I
   a. cheat him
   b. read to him
   c. protect him
   d. draw a picture of him

10. A factory is likely to **discharge**
    a. prisoners
    b. metal parts
    c. rifles
    d. smoke

11. I would expect my **confederates** to
    a. work together with me
    b. make fun of me
    c. refuse to help me
    d. plot against me

12. Which of these is a cat most likely to **pursue**?
    a. a dream
    b. a mouse
    c. a dog
    d. a career in television

Definitions

Study the spelling, pronunciation, part of speech, and definition given for each of the words below. Write the word in the blank space in the sentence that follows. Then read the synonyms and antonyms.

1. **complicate**
   (käm' plə kāt)

   (v.) to make hard to understand or do
   A lot of unnecessary details can sometimes ____complicate____ directions.

   SYNONYMS: to confuse, muddle, mix up
   ANTONYMS: to simplify, clarify, smooth, ease

2. **courteous**
   (kûr' tē əs)

   (adj.) considerate toward others
   A ____courteous____ host is sure to greet all guests and make them feel welcome.

   SYNONYMS: polite, well-mannered, respectful, civil
   ANTONYMS: rude, impolite, ill-mannered, discourteous

3. **discomfort**
   (dis kum' fərt)

   (n.) a lack of ease and well-being
   A nasty case of chicken pox can cause a great deal of ____discomfort____.

   SYNONYMS: pain, distress, irritation, suffering
   ANTONYMS: comfort, peace, calm

4. **eliminate**
   (i li' mə nāt)

   (v.) to get rid of or do away with
   If we all work together, we can ____eliminate____ hunger and poverty.

   SYNONYMS: to remove, omit, leave out, exclude, drop
   ANTONYMS: to take in, admit, acquire, retain, preserve

5. **grieve**
   (grēv)

   (v.) to cause to feel great sadness; to feel very sad
   Reports of the many deaths and the destruction caused by the earthquake ____grieve____ us all.

   SYNONYMS: to sadden, mourn, regret
   ANTONYMS: to rejoice, celebrate, gladden

6. **moral**
   (môr' əl)

   (adj.) having to do with what is right and wrong; being good and just
   A ____moral____ question is sometimes very difficult to answer.
   (n.) the lesson taught by a story or experience
   I think that the ____moral____ of the story is "never give up."

   SYNONYMS: (adj.) honorable, upright, honest; (n.) a message, teaching
   ANTONYMS: (adj.) immoral, wicked, bad, wrong

Internet For vocabulary games and activities, visit www.sadlier-oxford.com.

Millions of people visit New York every year to view the **spectacle** (word 9) of the Manhattan skyline.

7. scorch
(skôrch)

(v.) to burn on the surface; to dry out with heat
Did you _____ scorch _____ my brand-new shirt with the iron?

(n.) a slight burn
I placed the napkin so it would cover a _____ scorch _____ in the tablecloth.

SYNONYMS: (v.) to singe, brown, blacken, shrivel

8. severe
(sə vēr′)

(adj.) of a serious nature; very strict and harsh; causing pain or hardship
Most parents think lying is a _____ severe _____ offense.

SYNONYMS: grave, stern; tough, bitter; brutal, rough
ANTONYMS: unimportant; mild; merciful

9. spectacle
(spek′ ti kəl)

(n.) an unusual sight or public display
An eclipse of the sun is an awesome _____ spectacle _____.

SYNONYMS: a scene, show, exhibition, marvel

10. tragic
(tra′ jik)

(adj.) having to do with a serious story with a sad ending; very unfortunate
Stories with _____ tragic _____ endings make me cry.

SYNONYMS: dreadful, awful, sad, disastrous, unhappy
ANTONYMS: amusing, funny, humorous, comical, happy

11. trifle
(trī′ fəl)

(n.) something of little importance; a small amount
It is not worth arguing over such a _____ trifle _____.

(v.) to treat carelessly or playfully
It is unkind to _____ trifle _____ with someone's feelings.

SYNONYMS: (n.) a bit, knickknack, trinket; (v.) to fiddle, play, toy
ANTONYMS: (n.) a lot, lots of

12. universal
(yü nə vûr′ səl)

(adj.) being everywhere; of, for, or shared by all
Food and shelter are _____ universal _____ needs.

SYNONYMS: worldwide, broad, general, widespread
ANTONYMS: local, limited, narrow

For each item below, choose the word whose meaning is suggested by the clue given. Then write the word in the space provided.

1. To feel great sadness over a loss is to _____ grieve _____.
   a. scorch   b. trifle   c. grieve   d. eliminate

2. When you make a task harder, you _____ complicate _____ it.
   a. complicate   b. eliminate   c. scorch   d. grieve for

3. If your throat is sore, you might feel _____ discomfort _____.
   a. moral   b. discomfort   c. scorch   d. spectacle

4. Joy that is shared by everyone in the world is _____ universal _____.
   a. tragic   b. severe   c. universal   d. moral

5. Someone who is considerate of other people's feelings is _____ courteous _____.
   a. courteous   b. moral   c. severe   d. tragic

6. During a dry spell the sun may _____ scorch _____ the earth.
   a. complicate   b. eliminate   c. trifle with   d. scorch

7. A fatal accident is a _____ tragic _____ event.
   a. moral   b. courteous   c. tragic   d. universal

8. A very strict or harsh king is a _____ severe _____ ruler.
   a. universal   b. severe   c. courteous   d. tragic

9. A life that is good and just is a _____ moral _____ one.
   a. moral   b. severe   c. tragic   d. universal

10. A small amount of something is a _____ trifle _____.
    a. discomfort   b. moral   c. spectacle   d. trifle

11. To get rid of something is to _____ eliminate _____ it.
    a. complicate   b. grieve for   c. trifle with   d. eliminate

12. A public display, such as fireworks, is a _____ spectacle _____.
    a. trifle   b. spectacle   c. discomfort   d. moral

Synonyms

*For each item below, choose the word that is most nearly the **same** in meaning as the word or phrase in **boldface**. Then write your choice on the line provided.*

1. caused great **distress**
   a. spectacle   b. trifle   c. discomfort   d. moral   _____discomfort_____

2. a grand **scene**
   a. moral   b. spectacle   c. trifle   d. discomfort   _____spectacle_____

3. the **message** of the fable
   a. trifle   b. scorch   c. spectacle   d. moral   _____moral_____

4. **burned** the grass
   a. scorched   b. eliminated   c. complicated   d. grieved for   _____scorched_____

5. **fiddle** with the rules
   a. complicate   b. scorch   c. eliminate   d. trifle   _____trifle_____

6. **leave out** the negative comments
   a. eliminate   b. complicate   c. trifle with   d. grieve for   _____eliminate_____

Antonyms

*For each item below, choose the word that is most nearly **opposite** in meaning to the word or phrase in **boldface**. Then write your choice on the line provided.*

1. **simplify** things
   a. scorch   b. complicate   c. eliminate   d. trifle with   _____complicate_____

2. a **mild** winter
   a. severe   b. moral   c. universal   d. courteous   _____severe_____

3. having **limited** appeal
   a. tragic   b. severe   c. moral   d. universal   _____universal_____

4. **amusing** love stories
   a. universal   b. courteous   c. tragic   d. moral   _____tragic_____

5. a **rude** customer
   a. severe   b. universal   c. courteous   d. tragic   _____courteous_____

6. **rejoice** with the family
   a. trifle   b. grieve   c. scorch   d. eliminate   _____grieve_____

Completing the Sentence

From the list of words on pages 128–129, choose the one that best completes each item below. Then write the word in the space provided. (You may have to change the word's ending.)

From the list of words on pages 128–129

DEATH OF A PRESIDENT

■ When President John F. Kennedy was killed by an assassin's bullet on November 22, 1963, the _____ tragic _____ event shocked the nation. The President was only forty-five years old.

■ Americans _____ grieved _____ openly as they watched his formal state funeral on television or listened to it on the radio.

■ People still recall the respectful and _____ courteous _____ behavior of the huge crowds that lined the funeral route.

WHY SAVE THE RAIN FORESTS?

■ The magnificent variety of animals and plants in the tropical rain forests creates a _____ spectacle _____ unlike anything else in nature.

■ The effort to protect these forests is _____ complicated _____ by the need to use some of the valuable resources found in them, such as medicines.

■ When any plant or animal is forever _____ eliminated _____ from the earth, the balance of nature changes. The loss of a single species may result in harm to many more.

■ One result of a change in the balance of nature can be a _____ universal _____ shift in weather patterns. A change that at first has only local effects may in time affect the whole world.

■ Many people now regard destruction of the rain forests as a _____ moral _____ issue, not just a political or legal one, because it can ruin the future of the entire planet.

SUNBURN REALLY HURTS

■ Many people do not realize how easily they can _____ scorch _____ their skin just by walking or playing outside on a sunny day.

■ Even on a cloudy day, it is possible to get a _____ severe _____ sunburn.

■ If you get a painful sunburn, ask your doctor what you should do to ease the _____ discomfort _____.

■ Always remember that a sunburn is nothing to _____ trifle _____ with. It can cause serious harm to your skin.

Word Associations

*Circle the letter next to the word or expression that best completes the sentence or answers the question. Pay special attention to the word in **boldface**.*

1. A **courteous** bus driver might
   a. yell at passengers
   b. greet each passenger
   c. wear gloves while driving
   d. pass your bus stop on purpose

2. A **severe** cold spell would
   a. cause great hardship
   b. delight all skiers
   c. make people sleepy
   d. not last long

3. A **tragic** event might make you
   a. jump for joy
   b. break a leg
   c. weep with sadness
   d. go to a movie

4. If you feel **discomfort**, you should
   a. turn off the lights
   b. whistle in the dark
   c. rest for an hour
   d. seek relief

5. Which of these is a **universal** human experience?
   a. raising camels
   b. becoming an astronaut
   c. owning a rice plantation
   d. being born

6. Which is the **moral** of a story?
   a. "Slow and steady wins the race."
   b. "Do not fold, tear, or cut."
   c. "Dogs are related to wolves."
   d. "Why can't people fly?"

7. A **complicated** explanation is
   a. easy to understand
   b. likely to be false
   c. always helpful
   d. hard to follow

8. **Scorched** milk is sure to taste
   a. spicy
   b. sweet
   c. burnt
   d. refreshing

9. To **eliminate** sugar from your diet, you can
   a. add more salt
   b. learn how to cook
   c. cut out sweets
   d. drink lots of water

10. Which of these is a **trifle**?
    a. a party favor
    b. a huge weapon
    c. a million dollars
    d. a banquet

11. Which is a **spectacle**?
    a. a pair of glasses
    b. a three-ring circus
    c. an empty football field
    d. a bowl of vanilla ice cream

12. People usually **grieve** at
    a. birthday parties
    b. family funerals
    c. political rallies
    d. baseball games

Definitions Study the spelling, pronunciation, part of speech, and definition given for each of the words below. Write the word in the blank space in the sentence that follows. Then read the synonyms and antonyms.

1. **assume**
   (ə süm')

   (v.) to take upon oneself; to take for oneself; to pretend to have or be; to take for granted

   My parents said I could have the puppy if I would _____assume_____ the responsibility for it.

   SYNONYMS: to accept, undertake, seize; to imagine, suppose, believe
   ANTONYMS: to reject, refuse, give up

2. **cram**
   (kram)

   (v.) to stuff tightly; to fill tightly; to study hard just before a test

   Mom told me not to _____cram_____ all my clothes into one drawer.

   SYNONYMS: to pack, crowd, jam, load, squeeze
   ANTONYMS: to empty, clean out, clear out

3. **endanger**
   (in dān' jər)

   (v.) to expose to injury or harm

   Fire and drought _____endanger_____ our forests and the animals that live in them.

   SYNONYMS: to risk, threaten
   ANTONYMS: to protect, defend, preserve, save, secure

4. **fare**
   (fâr)

   (v.) to get along

   If you study hard, you should _____fare_____ well in school.

   (n.) the cost of travel on public transportation; food and drink

   Dad called to find out the plane _____fare_____ from Los Angeles to New York.

   SYNONYMS: (v.) to manage, succeed; (n.) a charge, fee, price; a menu

5. **fertile**
   (fûr' təl)

   (adj.) good for producing crops and plants; capable of developing or growing

   The rich farmland of the Midwest makes it one of the most _____fertile_____ areas in the world.

   SYNONYMS: fruitful, productive, rich
   ANTONYMS: barren, unproductive

6. **furnish**
   (fûr' nish)

   (v.) to supply with furniture; to supply with what is needed

   After the fire damage was repaired, neighbors pitched in to help _____furnish_____ the house.

   SYNONYMS: to equip, outfit, provide, give
   ANTONYMS: to take, withhold

One of the most **fertile** (word 5) areas in the world is the Midwest, sometimes called "America's Breadbasket."

7. mammoth
(ma' məth)

(n.) a very large, long-tusked, shaggy-haired elephant that is now extinct
The last woolly _____ mammoth _____ *died thousands of years ago.*

(adj.) great in size
A skyscraper is a _____ mammoth _____ *building.*

SYNONYMS: (adj.) enormous, huge, immense, gigantic, colossal
ANTONYMS: (adj.) small, tiny, little, miniature

8. peer
(pēr)

(n.) a person of the same age, rank, or ability; a British noble
As a gifted pianist, the child had no _____ peer _____ .

(v.) to look closely at
I tend to _____ peer _____ *at people through my glasses.*

SYNONYMS: (n.) an equal, colleague; (v.) to gaze, stare, scan

9. rigid
(ri' jəd)

(adj.) not bending; very strict
Stand at attention, and keep your body _____ rigid _____ .

SYNONYMS: stiff, firm, inflexible; severe, stern
ANTONYMS: elastic, flexible, loose

10. rowdy
(raŭ' dē)

(adj.) rough and disorderly
My teacher does not tolerate _____ rowdy _____ *behavior.*

SYNONYMS: wild, unruly, noisy
ANTONYMS: quiet, tame, gentle, mild

11. safeguard
(sāf' gärd)

(n.) something that protects
A helmet is a _____ safeguard _____ *against head injuries.*

(v.) to protect against possible danger
Wear sunblock to _____ safeguard _____ *your skin.*

SYNONYMS: (n.) a protection, defense; (v.) to defend, guard, save
ANTONYMS: (v.) to endanger, threaten, risk

12. trespass
(*n.,* tres' pəs;
v., tres' pas)

(n.) an action that is wrong; unlawful entry onto someone's property
The man was charged with criminal _____ trespass _____ .

(v.) to do wrong; to enter onto someone's property without right
I did not mean to _____ trespass _____ *against you.*

SYNONYMS: (n.) a sin, wrongdoing; an invasion; (v.) to sin, offend, intrude

135

Match the Meaning

For each item below, choose the word whose meaning is suggested by the clue given. Then write the word in the space provided.

1. If I put people at risk, I _____ endanger _____ their lives.
   a. cram   b. safeguard   c. assume   d. endanger

2. A noisy and wild party may be described as _____ rowdy _____.
   a. mammoth   b. rowdy   c. fertile   d. rigid

3. A member of British royalty is a _____ peer _____.
   a. peer   b. safeguard   c. mammoth   d. fare

4. To take something for granted is to _____ assume _____ it is so.
   a. cram   b. assume   c. furnish   d. endanger

5. When I eat bread and cheese for lunch, I dine on simple _____ fare _____.
   a. safeguards   b. mammoths   c. fare   d. trespasses

6. A large, extinct "woolly" elephant is called a _____ mammoth _____.
   a. mammoth   b. safeguard   c. peer   d. fare

7. If a lot of people get on a bus or train, they _____ cram _____ into it.
   a. furnish   b. assume   c. safeguard   d. cram

8. A person who is very strict may be described as _____ rigid _____.
   a. rowdy   b. rigid   c. mammoth   d. fertile

9. If I protect people from risk, I _____ safeguard _____ their lives.
   a. assume   b. endanger   c. safeguard   d. furnish

10. An egg that can develop into a chick is one that is _____ fertile _____.
    a. fertile   b. rowdy   c. mammoth   d. rigid

11. To enter someone's property without first getting permission is to _____ trespass _____.
    a. cram   b. endanger   c. trespass   d. peer

12. If I supply necessary information, I _____ furnish _____ the facts.
    a. safeguard   b. endanger   c. assume   d. furnish

Synonyms

*For each item below, choose the word that is most nearly the **same** in meaning as the word or phrase in **boldface**. Then write your choice on the line provided.*

1. **stare** through the window
   a. cram   b. trespass   c. peer   d. assume   _____ peer _____

2. **rich** soil
   a. rigid   b. fertile   c. rowdy   d. mammoth   _____ fertile _____

3. **defend** the planet
   a. furnish   b. endanger   c. cram   d. safeguard   _____ safeguard _____

4. collect the **fee**
   a. mammoth   b. fare   c. safeguard   d. peer   _____ fare _____

5. **equip** the lab
   a. furnish   b. endanger   c. cram   d. safeguard   _____ furnish _____

6. **intrude** on private property
   a. peer   b. assume   c. trespass   d. cram   _____ trespass _____

Antonyms

*For each item below, choose the word that is most nearly **opposite** in meaning to the word or phrase in **boldface**. Then write your choice on the line provided.*

1. **small** in size
   a. rigid   b. mammoth   c. rowdy   d. fertile   _____ mammoth _____

2. a **quiet** activity
   a. rigid   b. fertile   c. mammoth   d. rowdy   _____ rowdy _____

3. a **flexible** rule
   a. mammoth   b. rowdy   c. fertile   d. rigid   _____ rigid _____

4. **empty** your locker
   a. furnish   b. safeguard   c. cram   d. endanger   _____ cram _____

5. **protect** the spotted owl
   a. cram   b. endanger   c. furnish   d. safeguard   _____ endanger _____

6. **give up** control
   a. furnish   b. safeguard   c. assume   d. endanger   _____ assume _____

Completing the Sentence

From the list of words on pages 134–135, choose the one that best completes each item below. Write the word in the space provided. (You may have to change the word's ending.)

From the list of words on pages 134–135

A BIG MISTAKE

■ I made a big mistake when I _____assumed_____ that I could wait until the night before the big test to start studying. I should have known better than to take it for granted that I would do well on the test.

■ My _____peers_____ teased me when I told them that I was worried about the test. They said I didn't need to study hard. Now I know that I shouldn't have listened to them.

■ I had to stay up very late to _____cram_____ my brain full of facts and figures. When I realized how much I needed to learn, I began to feel sick with panic.

■ To make matters worse, the people in the house next door had a _____rowdy_____ party that lasted until one o'clock in the morning. I couldn't sleep because of the noise.

■ The next day I was so tired that I couldn't remember anything. So it was no surprise that I _____fared_____ badly on the test.

SAVE THE WETLANDS

■ America's wetlands provide a rich and _____fertile_____ environment for thousands of species of plants and animals.

■ But pollution and development more and more _____endanger_____ these beautiful places. In some areas their very survival is at risk.

■ If we lose our wetlands, many of the creatures that live there will become as extinct as the woolly _____mammoth_____.

■ Lots of concerned individuals and organizations are working to educate the public about how important it is to _____safeguard_____ this precious natural resource.

SAFETY IN A DANGEROUS PLACE

■ Scientists who study deadly viruses work in special laboratories where strict safety measures are enforced. There are _____rigid_____ rules to protect all the employees.

■ All workers are _____furnished_____ with special protective clothing that they must put on before going into the lab.

■ Only employees are allowed to enter the lab. Anyone who tries to get into one of these "hot zones" without proper identification will be considered to be _____trespassing_____. Security guards will escort intruders from the building.

Word Associations

Circle the letter next to the word or expression that best completes the sentence or answers the question. Pay special attention to the word in **boldface.**

1. A **fertile** animal may give birth to
   a. many young
   b. green plants
   c. good ideas
   d. fruits or vegetables

2. A jury of your **peers** would be made up of
   a. two dukes
   b. your parents
   c. other students
   d. telescopes

3. A **rowdy** greeting is likely to be
   a. stern
   b. loud
   c. gentle
   d. whispered

4. Which is a **safeguard** against theft?
   a. a burglar alarm
   b. sunscreen
   c. lifeguard
   d. deodorant soap

5. Which usually requires paying a **fare**?
   a. a skateboard ride
   b. a taxi ride
   c. a car ride
   d. a sled ride

6. One who **assumes** a brave manner is
   a. bragging
   b. fighting
   c. shouting
   d. pretending

7. A **crammed** suitcase is probably
   a. well organized
   b. half full
   c. hard to close
   d. locked

8. One way to say "No **Trespassing**" is
   a. "Closed for Repairs"
   b. "Keep Out"
   c. "Out of Business"
   d. "This Way to Exit"

9. If I **furnish** food for a picnic, I
   a. invite the ants
   b. set up the lawn furniture
   c. eat the lion's share
   d. bring lots to eat

10. A **mammoth** corporation probably has
    a. a large board of directors
    b. many elephants
    c. lions, tigers, and bears
    d. a small parking lot

11. An **endangered** species is
    a. threatened by extinction
    b. dangerous to others
    c. safe from harm
    d. protected by mammoths

12. Which of these is **rigid**?
    a. a rubber band
    b. a mound of jello
    c. a soap bubble
    d. a steel beam

REVIEW UNITS 13–16

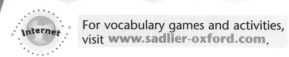

For vocabulary games and activities, visit **www.sadlier-oxford.com**.

Selecting Word Meanings — For each of the following items, circle the choice that is most nearly the **same** in meaning as the word in **boldface** type in the introductory phrase.

1. an important scientific **achievement**
   a. failure   b. principle   c. method   d. accomplishment

2. **furnish** proof of ownership
   a. supply   b. copy   c. lose   d. request

3. an inexpensive **trifle**
   a. gift   b. trinket   c. meal   d. weapon

4. a **singular** opportunity
   a. welcome   b. missed   c. unusual   d. lucky

5. a **moral** decision
   a. wicked   b. reasonable   c. just   d. difficult

6. arrested the **confederates**
   a. accomplices   b. witnesses   c. victims   d. enemies

7. **swindle** the tourist
   a. help   b. cheat   c. meet   d. entertain

8. **grieved** for the victims
   a. worked   b. rejoiced   c. searched   d. mourned

9. **endanger** the public's health
   a. ignore   b. protect   c. threaten   d. study

10. **sanitary** medical instruments
   a. filthy   b. sterile   c. new   d. used

11. an **economical** means of transportation
   a. thrifty   b. safe   c. comfortable   d. costly

12. a bitter **debate**
   a. medicine   b. person   c. taste   d. argument

Spelling

For each item below, study the **boldface** word in which there is a blank. If a letter is missing, fill in the blank to make a correctly spelled word. If the word is already spelled correctly, leave the blank empty.

1. **spra_w_l** in a hammock
2. **tres__pass** on my land
3. **re_i_gn** over France
4. a **ro__wdy** mob
5. a **tra_g_ic** mistake
6. **a_c_quire** knowledge

7. a **fertil_e_** imagination
8. **s_c_orch** the linen
9. **safeg_u_ard** the passengers
10. a **mono__tonous** story
11. **mod_i_fy** the instructions
12. **clim_i_nate** the problem

Antonyms

For each of the following items, circle the choice that is most nearly the **opposite** in meaning to the word in **boldface** type in the introductory phrase.

1. the **latter** part of the year
   a. earlier ⟵
   b. warmest
   c. last
   d. largest

2. show signs of **discomfort**
   a. excitement
   b. irritation
   c. interest
   d. calm ⟵

3. **cram** the theater aisles
   a. crowd
   b. clear out ⟵
   c. stand in
   d. walk down

4. a **courteous** note
   a. unsigned
   b. polite
   c. short
   d. rude ⟵

5. **preserve** the landmark building
   a. save
   b. paint
   c. destroy ⟵
   d. enlarge

6. rise up in **mutiny**
   a. support ⟵
   b. song
   c. rebellion
   d. anger

7. **complicate** the assignment
   a. confuse
   b. complete
   c. change
   d. simplify ⟵

8. a **negative** attitude
   a. friendly
   b. positive ⟵
   c. bad
   d. peculiar

Vocabulary for Comprehension

*Read the following passage in which some of the words you have studied appear in **boldface**. Then answer the questions on page 143.*

The Experience of a Lifetime

Carl, Anna, and their parents joined the crowd in the station. They had prepared for this day since March. Carl earned money doing the morning milking. Anna baked pies and biscuits. The family was careful to save every penny toward the train **fare** and the admission fee. At last, they were ready for the greatest celebration of the century—the 1893 Chicago World's Fair. They joined travelers from all over the world, eager to see the **spectacle** on Lake Michigan.

The train was nearly full when it entered the station. The crowd was quick to board. Anna clutched Carl's hand as Mom and Dad guided them toward a seat. After an hour's rattling ride, the train was at the fair's main gate.

Carl whistled. Anna gasped in awe. Tens of thousands of visitors were strolling the walkways. People toured halls **crammed** with **exhibits**. Anna and Carl stopped to see a gigantic cheese from Canada. It weighed in at 22,000 pounds! "C'mon, kids," Dad exclaimed. "Let's find the trained lions from Africa, the electric dishwashing machine, and the United States map that's made entirely of pickles!"

"First, the wheel," said Carl with enthusiasm.

"The wheel?" Anna asked.

Ferris wheel on the grounds of the 1893 World's Fair

"You know. The one by George Ferris, the genius engineer from Pittsburgh," Carl answered. "Maybe we can ride twice!"

The family headed toward the wondrous wheel, which towered over everything else. It was huge! Its 36 wooden cars carried 2,160 people high above the ground for a thrilling 20-minute view of the **sprawling** exhibition grounds. Carl and Anna took their places on the long line for the ride of a lifetime.

Fill in the circle next to the choice that best completes the sentence or answers the question.

1. This passage was mainly written to
   (a) encourage tourism to Chicago
   (b) provide a glimpse into the future
   (c) describe the creation of the Ferris wheel
   (d) provide a picture of the World's Fair of 1893

2. The events take place at
   (a) the fairgrounds in Chicago
   (b) a lake in Canada
   (c) an amusement park in Michigan
   (d) a train station in Pittsburgh

3. In this passage, **fare** means
   (a) manage
   (b) charge
   (c) menu
   (d) route

4. A **spectacle** is a(n)
   (a) luxury boat
   (b) grand public display
   (c) dance performance
   (d) impressive sunrise

5. From the passage, you can tell that Carl and Anna live
   (a) on or near a farm
   (b) in an apartment house
   (c) in Chicago
   (d) near Lake Michigan

6. When Carl and Anna were roaming the fair, you could say they were
   (a) displeased
   (b) overjoyed
   (c) fearful
   (d) frantic

7. Another word for **crammed** is
   (a) packed
   (b) furnished
   (c) littered
   (d) preserved

8. The **exhibits** in this passage are
   (a) paintings from an art class
   (b) displays shown to the public
   (c) preserves for wild animals
   (d) amazing stories

9. According to Carl, the highlight of the fair is the
   (a) trained lions
   (b) gigantic cheese
   (c) electric dishwashing machine
   (d) Ferris wheel

10. **Sprawling** most nearly means
    (a) narrow
    (b) scenic
    (c) spread out
    (d) elaborate

Grammar in Context

A **verb** and its **subject** must **agree** in number. This means that if the subject is singular, the verb must be singular. If the subject is plural, the verb must be plural.

The verb **be** does not show action. It tells what the subject is or is like. Use the form of **be** that agrees with the subject.

Subject	Present Tense	Past Tense
I	am	was
he, she, it, or singular noun	is	was
you, we, they, or plural noun	are	were

Read the sentences in the box. Notice how the subject and verb in each sentence agree.

> The crowd was quick to board.   We are thrilled.
>
> People were ready for the celebration.   He is a genius.

*Choose the verb in **boldface** that correctly completes the sentence. Then write the sentence on the line.*

1. Anna (**is, are**) grateful for the invitation to the exhibit. Anna is grateful for the invitation to the exhibit.

2. Carl (**was, were**) courteous and thanked the man. Carl was courteous and thanked the man.

3. The mammoth displays (**was, were**) magnificent. The mammoth displays were magnificent.

4. The metal frames (**is, are**) a little rusty but still rigid. The metal frames are a little rusty but still rigid.

5. The fair (**was, were**) an enormous achievement. The fair was an enormous achievement.

Completing the Idea

Complete each sentence so that it makes sense. Pay attention to the word in **boldface.**

Accept answers that show an understanding of the vocabulary.

1. The crowd became **rowdy** when _____.

2. When I **acquire** my new bike, I will _____.

3. It is so **monotonous** to listen to _____.

4. One way to maintain **sanitary** conditions is to _____.

5. To be perfectly **frank**, I wish _____.

6. I want to **modify** my speech because _____.

7. I might **pursue** a job in which I _____.

8. Three examples of **singular** nouns are _____.

9. To do well on the test, I must **furnish** _____.

10. New shoes may cause great **discomfort** because _____.

11. You might **scorch** the toast if you _____.

12. It is normal to **grieve** after _____.

13. In **fertile** soil, you can expect to _____.

14. Use a small mirror to **peer** into _____.

15. When a sign says "Do Not **Trespass**," you'd better _____.

Write Your Own

Choose a word from Units 13–16. Write a sentence using the word.
Be sure to correct any errors in subject-verb agreement.

Check that the vocabulary is used correctly and that the sentence is written correctly.

_____

*The words in **boldface** in the sentences below are related to words introduced in Units 13–16. For example, the adjectives* trifling *and* spectacular *in item 1 are related to the nouns* trifle *and* spectacle *(both in Unit 15). Based on your understanding of the unit words that follow, circle the related word in **boldface** that best completes each sentence.*

acquire	assume	complicate	courteous	eliminate
exhibit	furnish	modify	monotonous	moral
preserve	pursue	rigid	rowdy	severe
singular	spectacle	tragic	trifle	universal

1. One reason for a movie's success at the box office may be its (**trifling**/ **spectacular**) special effects.

2. Several rooms in the museum display (**furnishings**/**complications**) from colonial America.

3. Scientists all over the world are working for the (**preservation**/**assumption**) of endangered animals such as the giant panda, the tiger, and the tamarins of the Amazon rain forests.

4. Americans believe that the (**courtesy**/**pursuit**) of happiness is a basic human right.

5. Because of the (**severity**/**rowdiness**) of the blizzard, highways were closed, and flights were canceled.

6. Museum officials held a press conference to announce the (**modification**/ **acquisition**) of an important painting by Picasso.

7. Last fall my English class attended a performance of a (**tragedy**/**morality**) by William Shakespeare.

8. When I have a boring chore to do, I like to listen to music to relieve the (**monotony**/**singularity**) of the task.

9. A highlight of this year's science fair was an (**elimination**/**exhibition**) of crystals and minerals.

10. The popular author's new novel was widely praised for the (**universality**/ **rigidity**) of its story.

Use the clue and the given letters to complete each word. Write the missing letters of the word in the appropriate boxes. Then use the circled letters and the drawing to find the CHALLENGE word.

1. Rather unusual!

(S) I N G U L A (R)

2. An occasion for pro and con

D (E) B (A) T E

3. Another word for an English noble

(P) E E R

4. How would you describe a person who is polite and thoughtful?

C O U R T E O U (S)

5. Don't bother me with such an unimportant matter.

(T) R I F L E

6. A hospital operating room should always be this.

(S) A N I T A R Y

Challenge:

If I disobey this sign, what would I do?

T R E S P A S S

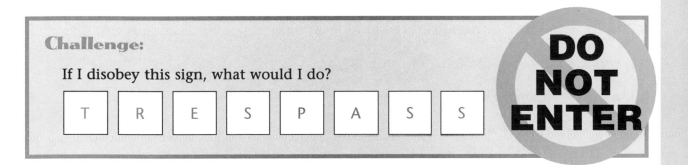

DO NOT ENTER

Definitions *Choose the word from the box that matches each definition. Write the word on the line provided.*

abolish	abuse	appeal	avalanche	brittle
dictator	displace	gauge	massacre	migrant
nestle	portable	preserve	rigid	scorch
selective	singular	spectacle	tragic	vicinity

1. an unusual sight or public display   spectacle

2. to settle down comfortably; to hold lovingly   nestle

3. not bending; very strict   rigid

4. a ruler or leader who has total power   dictator

5. to kill many people or animals in a cruel way   massacre

6. out of the ordinary   singular

7. the area near a place, the surrounding region   vicinity

8. to measure; to estimate   gauge

9. easily moved or carried   portable

10. improper, wrong, or cruel treatment   abuse

11. to force to move or flee; to move out of position   displace

12. very careful about choosing or using   selective

13. a sincere or strong request for something   appeal

14. to burn on the surface; to dry out with heat   scorch

15. very unfortunate   tragic

Antonyms

Choose the word from the box that is most nearly **opposite** in meaning to each group of words. Write the word on the line provided.

1. divided, separated; a foe	confederate	absurd
2. unlike, different	identical	achievement
3. to lose, give up, surrender	acquire	acquire
4. quiet, tame, gentle	rowdy	brisk
5. feast, plenty	famine	cherish
6. kindhearted, merciful	pitiless	confederate
7. to hate, despise, dishonor	cherish	discharge
8. local, limited, narrow	universal	downfall
9. to detain; to hire; to load	discharge	endanger
10. a defeat, failure, setback	achievement	expand
11. barren, unproductive	fertile	famine
12. to run away (from), flee	pursue	fertile
13. sensible, wise, intelligent	absurd	grieve
14. a hunter, predator	prey	humiliate
15. wicked, bad, wrong	moral	identical
16. to protect, defend, preserve	endanger	monotonous
17. varied, lively, exciting	monotonous	moral
18. to rejoice, celebrate, gladden	grieve	negative
19. slow, dull, sluggish	brisk	pitiless
20. to shrink, reduce, contract	expand	prey
		pursue
		rowdy
		safeguard
		security
		universal

Completing the Sentence

Choose the word from the box that best completes each sentence below. Write the word in the space provided.

Group A

courteous	descend	economical	flimsy
latter	modify	navigate	rotate

1. Believe it or not, it may be harder to _____ **descend** _____ a steep hill than to climb it.

2. I carefully read the first part of the book, but I only skimmed the _____ **latter** _____ half.

3. You're not a true sailor until you are able to _____ **navigate** _____ choppy waters.

4. You're likely to feel cold if you wear a(n) _____ **flimsy** _____ jacket on a cool autumn night.

5. I waved to thank the _____ **courteous** _____ driver who let us cross the street.

Group B

alibi	confirm	fare	plea
principle	shred	soothe	trespass

1. I begged my parents to extend my curfew, but my _____ **plea** _____ fell on deaf ears.

2. My teacher will not accept "The dog ate my homework" as a(n) _____ **alibi** _____ for not handing in an assignment.

3. I'll call the airline to _____ **confirm** _____ our reservations so we'll be sure to have seats on the flight.

4. You'll need exact change to pay the _____ **fare** _____ when you board the bus.

5. Would you prefer creamy vanilla ice cream or hot tea with honey to _____ **soothe** _____ your sore throat?

Classifying

Choose the word from the box that goes best with each group of words. Write the word in the space provided. Then explain what the words have in common.

assume	daze	discomfort	foe	frank
mammoth	presentable	realistic	reign	tart

1. acceptable, enjoyable, _____presentable_____

   The words end with the same suffix.

2. dodo, passenger pigeon, saber-toothed tiger, _____mammoth_____

   The words name extinct animals.

3. bewilder, baffle, _____daze_____

   The words are synonyms.

4. real, _____realistic_____, reality, realize

   The words belong to the same family.

5. disorder, dishonor, _____discomfort_____

   The words begin with the same prefix.

6. blank, _____frank_____, sank, thank

   The words rhyme.

7. enemy, opponent, rival, _____foe_____

   The words are synonyms.

8. rain, rein, _____reign_____

   The words sound the same.

9. cookie, muffin, cake, _____tart_____

   The words name baked goods.

10. imagine, suppose, _____assume_____

    The words are synonyms.

Analogies

In each of the following, circle the letter for the item that best completes the comparison. Then explain the relationship on the lines provided.

1. **cherish** is to **abuse** as
   a. cuddle is to nestle
   b. displace is to move
   c. soothe is to excite
   d. end is to abolish

Relationship: "Cherish" and "abuse" are antonyms/opposite in meaning; "soothe" and "excite" are antonyms/opposite in meaning.

2. **flimsy** is to **weak** as
   a. realistic is to absurd
   b. tart is to sweet
   c. selective is to choosy
   d. pitiless is to caring

Relationship: "Flimsy" and "weak" are synonyms; "selective" and "choosy" are synonyms.

3. **attract** is to **appeal** as
   a. descend is to rise
   b. expand is to collapse
   c. plea is to forgive
   d. gauge is to measure

Relationship: "Attract" and "appeal" are synonyms; "gauge" and "measure" are synonyms.

4. **brittle** is to **flexible** as
   a. thrifty is to wasteful
   b. realistic is to practical
   c. tart is to tangy
   d. pitiless is to cruel

Relationship: "Brittle" and "flexible" are opposites/antonyms; "thrifty" and "wasteful" are opposites/antonyms.

5. **prey** is to **predator** as
   a. security is to doubt
   b. dictator is to tyrant
   c. plea is to appeal
   d. avalanche is to snow

Relationship: "Prey" and "predator" are opposites/antonyms; "security" and "doubt" are opposites/antonyms.

6. **famine** is to **food** as
   a. blizzard is to snow
   b. hurricane is to wind
   c. flood is to rain
   d. drought is to water

Relationship: A "famine" occurs when there is a shortage of "food"; a "drought" occurs when there is a shortage of "water."

7. foe is to **friend** as
- a. ally is to buddy
- b. moral is to message
- c. night is to day ✓
- d. rest is to relaxation

Relationship: _"Foe" and "friend" are_
antonyms/opposite in meaning; "night"
and "day" are antonyms/opposite in
meaning.

9. present is to **exhibit** as
- a. debate is to discuss ✓
- b. reject is to accept
- c. stay is to leave
- d. fail is to succeed

Relationship: _"Present" and "exhibit" are_
synonyms; "debate" and "discuss" are
synonyms.

8. humorous is to **tragic** as
- a. speedy is to quick
- b. prepared is to ready
- c. clean is to sanitary
- d. mammoth is to miniature ✓

Relationship: _"Humorous" and "tragic" are_
antonyms/opposites; "mammoth" and
"miniature" are antonyms/opposites.

10. mouse is to **singular** as
- a. trap is to mouse
- b. mice is to plural ✓
- c. mouse is to hole
- d. mice is to nice

Relationship: _"Mouse" is the "singular"_
form; "mice" is the "plural" form.

Challenge: Make up your own

Write a comparison using the words in the box below. (Hint: There are four possible analogies.) Then explain the relationship on the lines provided.

eat	fork	massacre	mutiny
negative	no	pencil	positive
revolt	slaughter	write	yes

A possible answer is given.

Analogy: ___slaughter___ is to ___massacre___ as ___revolt___ is to ___mutiny___.

Relationship: _"Slaughter" and "massacre" are synonyms; "revolt" and "mutiny" are_
synonyms.

Building with Latin and Greek Roots

A **root** is the part of the word that carries its meaning. Sometimes knowing the meaning of a root can help you figure out the meaning of an unknown word.

> **spec**—look
>
> The root **spec** appears in **spectacle**. A **spectacle** is a sight that looks impressive or unusual.

The words below contain the root **spec**. *Study the definition of each word. Then write the word on the line in the sample sentence.*

1. **prospect**   something that is looked forward to or expected

   I'm excited by the _____prospect_____ *of getting a new bike.*

2. **respect**   a high regard or consideration of the value of someone or something; to look at someone or something with high regard

   I _____respect_____ *your opinion even though I don't agree with it.*

3. **spectacular**   very unusual or impressive, making a great display

   The raging battle scenes in the film were _____spectacular_____.

4. **spectator**   a person who watches or looks but does not take part

   Not a single _____spectator_____ *left the final game of the World Series before the ninth inning.*

5. **suspect**   to consider that something is true, likely, or possible; a person who is thought to be guilty of a crime

   I _____suspect_____ *that the store has already closed.*

*Circle the word in **boldface** that best completes each sentence.*

1. We (**respect,** **suspect**) a trick is being played on us.

2. She earned everyone's (**prospect,** **respect**) for speaking out against the powerful politician.

3. The view of the Grand Canyon from the plane was (**spectacular,** **spectator**).

4. The (**prospect,** **suspect**) of moving to another country is both exciting and frightening.

5. Every (**spectacular,** **spectator**) gave the team a standing ovation.

From the list of words on page 154, choose the one that best completes each sentence below. Write the word on the line provided.

1. His fingerprints at the crime scene make him a prime _____suspect_____ for the burglary.

2. The bursts of color in the fireworks display were _____spectacular_____!

3. I have great _____respect_____ for your honesty and openness.

4. A _____spectator_____ from the visiting team waved her school banner at the game.

5. My sister is nervous about the _____prospect_____ of attending a new school.

Definitions — For each item, choose the word that matches the definition. Then write the word on the line provided.

1. to trick or lead a person into believing something that is not true
   a. blunder   b. displace   c. deceive   d. modify   deceive

2. weariness or exhaustion from work or lack of sleep
   a. feat   b. assault   c. discomfort   d. fatigue   fatigue

3. not correct; showing bad manners or taste
   a. improper   b. aggressive   c. severe   d. rigid   improper

4. to stun or confuse
   a. dispute   b. daze   c. gauge   d. debate   daze

5. easily broken or damaged, requiring special handling or care
   a. keen   b. flimsy   c. rigid   d. fragile   fragile

6. careful about spending money or using resources
   a. economical   b. moral   c. severe   d. energetic   economical

7. to cause to feel great sadness; to feel very sad
   a. enforce   b. justify   c. grieve   d. abuse   grieve

8. lasting or used for a limited time
   a. temporary   b. presentable   c. economical   d. moral   temporary

9. to stuff tightly; to fill tightly; to study hard just before a test
   a. distribute   b. bluff   c. classify   d. cram   cram

10. a discussion of reasons for and against something
    a. document   b. debate   c. plea   d. spectacle   debate

11. to plan or steer the course of a vessel or vehicle
    a. classify   b. emigrate   c. detect   d. navigate   navigate

12. a partner, friend
    a. confederate   b. associate   c. nomad   d. monarch   associate

13. easily broken, snapped, or cracked; not flexible
    a. tart   b. rigid   c. vivid   d. brittle   _____brittle_____

14. to turn around a central point; to alternate
    a. flexible   b. rotate   c. alternate   d. navigate   _____rotate_____

15. to show clearly; to put on display
    a. exhibit   b. detect   c. alternate   d. discharge   _____exhibit_____

16. avoiding unnecessary risks or mistakes
    a. frank   b. moral   c. rowdy   d. cautious   _____cautious_____

17. a friendly welcome and treatment of guests
    a. feat   b. hospitality c. alibi   d. fare   _____hospitality_____

18. to force obedience to
    a. acquire   b. dispute   c. ensure   d. enforce   _____enforce_____

19. to make calm; to ease pain or sorrow
    a. soothe   b. cherish   c. blunder   d. gauge   _____soothe_____

20. rough and disorderly
    a. energetic   b. shrewd   c. capable   d. rowdy   _____rowdy_____

 **Antonyms** *For each item below, indicate the part of speech of the word in* **boldface.** *In the space provided, write N for noun, V for verb, or A for adjective.*

21. __N__ felt the **jolt**

22. __A__ a **supreme** effort

23. __V__ **shred** the evidence

24. __N__ joined the **mutiny**

25. __V__ **cancel** the reservations

26. __N__ fled the **famine**

27. __N__ settle the **dispute**

28. __A__ a **courteous** manner

29. __V__ **sprawl** on the couch

30. __A__ a **hearty** laugh

 **Completing the Sentence**

Choose the word from the box that best completes each sentence. Write the word in the space provided. (You may have to change the word's ending.)

Group A

assume	cherish	confirm	fertile
postpone	reign	rigid	swindle

31. The mighty forces of nature can turn _____ fertile _____ farmland into a wasteland in which nothing will grow.

32. I will always _____ cherish _____ the memories of my visits to the Adirondacks.

33. It is the duty of the Senate to _____ confirm _____ or reject the President's appointments to the Supreme Court.

34. A team that _____ reigns _____ over a sport for several years is sometimes described as a "dynasty."

Group B

blemish	despise	feat	preserve
reliable	scorch	strategy	vast

35. The President promises to "_____ preserve _____, protect, and defend the Constitution of the United States."

36. Although the fire had _____ scorched _____ the letter, the writing could still be read.

37. It took many months for pioneers to cross the _____ vast _____ stretches of the American plains.

38. The best _____ strategy _____ for taking a test is to study hard so that you are as prepared for it as you can be.

*Circle the letter next to the word or expression that best completes the sentence or answers the question. Pay special attention to the word in **boldface.***

39. A **spectacle** might make you
    a. sleep
    b. fall
    c. stare
    d. eat

40. On a **bluff** you might
    a. go for a swim
    b. enjoy the view
    c. do your homework
    d. call a friend

41. Which should we **condemn**?
    a. cruelty
    b. kindness
    c. breakfast
    d. humor

42. Your **foe** is *not*
    a. your enemy
    b. your opponent
    c. your challenger
    d. your friend

43. Where would a **monarch** sit?
    a. on a throne
    b. in a court
    c. in a classroom
    d. in a highchair

44. Texas is in the **vicinity** of
    a. Canada
    b. India
    c. Mexico
    d. Spain

45. To **peer**, you need
    a. eyes
    b. ears
    c. thumbs
    d. toes

46. Who needs an **alibi**?
    a. a plumber
    b. a doctor
    c. a farmer
    d. a burglar

47. Which might you **classify**?
    a. trading cards
    b. pizzas
    c. sunsets
    d. gifts

48. With an **avalanche** comes
    a. good news
    b. mail
    c. snow
    d. coupons

49. A **solitary** walk is one
    a. that you take at night
    b. that you take barefoot
    c. that you take alone
    d. that you take after dinner

50. Which runs in a **primary**?
    a. a chicken
    b. a candidate
    c. a horse
    d. a dog

INDEX

The following is a list of all the words taught in the units of this book. The number after each entry indicates the page on which the word is first introduced, but the word also appears in exercises on later pages.